Secrets of a Recovering Perfectionist

Lessons From a Doctor, Mom, and Burnout Survivor

Denee Choice, MD

As a thank you for reading my book,
I'd like to offer you a FREE gift.

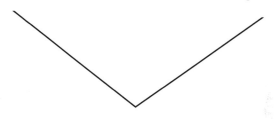

I created a Companion Guide to complement your learning
and personal growth as you read through the book.

To get your FREE copy of

Secrets of a Recovering Perfectionist
Companion Guide

Go to:
https://brainhealthmentor.com/secrets-of-a-recovering-
perfectionist/companion-guide/

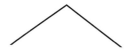

Dedication

This book is dedicated to all the driven, Type A, overachieving, perfectionist women out there who are trying to change the world.

While raising a family.

While having a life.

The world needs you and all the gifts you have to offer.

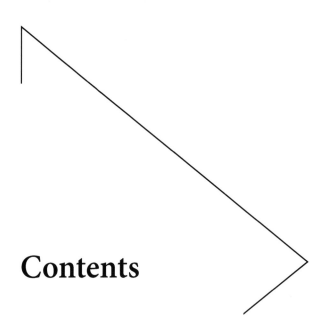

Contents

Part Two:

Master the Fundamentals: Eat, Move, Sleep

Part Three:

Tame the Stress Monster

Part Four: Hack Your Way Back

Part Five:

Etcetera

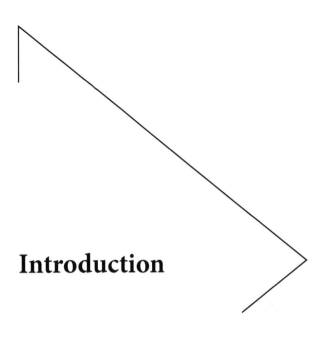

Introduction

Once upon a time, I was a thirty-something with a thriving medical career, a husband who worked crazy shifts, and two young children at home. Get up, feed the kids, get them to school, go to work, work a full day, pick up the kids. Shuttle them to soccer practice, go home and start dinner, pick them up after practice. Have dinner, clean up, get homework started, get the kids to bed. Crash in bed myself, exhausted. Get up the next day. Rinse and repeat.

Don't get me wrong; I loved my life. But it wasn't exactly the picture of balance and bliss. Was I burning the candle at both ends? Of course! Aren't we all? On the surface, it looked like I had it all together. Underneath, though, I was falling apart. Sounds familiar? If so, you're in the right place!

Despite being a doctor, I didn't always follow my own advice. Ever heard the saying, "Doctors make the worst patients?" So true! Also, the same is true for nurses, by the way. I routinely told my patients that they needed to exercise more, eat better, get more sleep and manage their stress.

I fully believed these actions promoted health, wellness, and balance. I still do. What was my excuse? Me? I was too busy, of course! Sound familiar?

So I did what you're doing. I powered through. I stayed on the hamster wheel, "succeeding" and "achieving" at work but barely holding it together in life. And it worked.

Until it didn't.

Eventually, running on the hamster wheel caught up with me. At first, my body started to show signs of weakness. I ignored the warnings and wrote them off as getting older. I still saw myself as healthy and active, and for the most part, I was. But the stress monster, which I had suppressed and ignored for far too many years, continued to grow. I kept telling myself it will get easier when the kids are in school; *It will get easier when the kids can drive; It will get easier when*…. You get the point.

I eventually left clinical medicine for a job in the corporate world. I think the overwhelm disappeared for a while, but as I succeeded in my new role and was promoted into bigger roles and opportunities, it crept back in. I had a job I loved, was aligned with the company's mission, and had a boss that I respected and admired.

And I said yes to every new opportunity along the way. I was back on the hamster wheel, working 60+ hour weeks, and that was just my day job.

Then my overachiever choices started to impact my mind. *That* was harder to ignore. I became overwhelmed with increasing responsibilities and expectations at work, and out of the blue, I started having trouble keeping everything straight. I was *way* too young to be having trouble with memory and concentration, so what the heck was going on?

As defined by the Miriam-Webster dictionary, burnout is "to cause to fail, wear out, or become exhausted especially from overwork or overuse. Originally applied to machinery, this word now applies to human health and wellness.

What I know now that I didn't realize then is that I was in the throes of burnout. It crept up when I wasn't looking. Chronic daily stress was a normal way of life for me and had been for many years. When I finally went to see my doctor, she asked me about my stress levels. I laughed it off and said I was fine. After all, *this was my normal.* Nothing had changed. Stress was for people who had "real" problems—people who lost their job, or were going through a divorce, or were dealing with serious illness. Not me—I was *fine.*

The body keeps score.

Except I wasn't. In truth, I had been running on empty for years, decades even, and just ignored it. Now it was catching up to me. I had to claw my way back out. And I did it. I did it without quitting my job and without going to an ashram in India for three months.

And if I can do it, you can do it, too. Full disclosure—there's no "fast pass" to instantly transport yourself back from burnout. You have to do the work. But I can help you get out faster than I did. This book lays out simple steps, the ones I learned by trial and error, that can get you on your road to recovery.

So here's a promise for you. I'm not gonna spew science at you. I'm not gonna dazzle you with the latest research. Because you're too busy, too. Instead, I'll tell you what did and didn't work for me with the hopes that the lessons I learned the hard way will prevent you from having to learn them for yourself.

I'll cut straight to the chase. Straight to the information that matters to you—what to do and how to do it. Period. And if you're inspired to learn more, I'm happy to point you to trusted resources where you can do your own reading and research—in your non-existent spare time.

Being a medical doctor, I am a scientist by training. I researched the literature, both scientific and pop culture health and wellness literature, along my path of recovery. This book is a result of what I learned, tried, and what worked for me. On my quest, I discovered some new skills and tools which have been game-changers for me in creating healthy habits that stick and moving the needle toward better health, less stress, and better balance in my life.

This is the secret sauce. And I can't wait to share it with you. If you follow the principles outlined here, they can work for you too. This is the roadmap I wish I'd had when I started my own journey.

One more thing.

I'm a doctor, but I'm not *your* doctor. Anything you learn in this book that you choose to try should be discussed with your doctor or healthcare team in the context of your own personal medical history, conditions, and risk factors. If you struggle with depression, anxiety, or other mental health challenges on top of stress, overwhelm, and perhaps burnout, don't try to DIY this; get the professional support you need.

As you read this book, don't think of me as a doctor. Think of me as a trusted friend. You know, one who tells you that you have spinach in your teeth, a bat in the cave, or that, yes, my friend, you're too old to share clothes with your teenage daughter. So let's get started!

Part One:
Awareness

Chapter 1
Houston, There's a Problem

You cannot solve a problem you're not willing to accept. ~ Todd Herman

In the introduction, I shared that despite being a medical doctor, I was in complete denial about my stress level. I didn't have a problem—I was fine. Just busy...you know. My high-achieving, Type A, and perfectionist tendencies not only contributed to my stress, they prevented me from admitting I had a problem. I was a fool, and I paid the price.

Don't be a fool. Here's the quick and dirty version of what you need to know about stress and burnout before we move into what you really want to know—what the heck to do about it.

Stress does not cause burnout. Your body's response to chronic stress leads to burnout.

Stress itself is not the problem. Stress is the normal physiologic response your body has to the demands placed upon it. If you're hiking in the woods and you come upon a bear, your body will automatically respond in one of three ways: fight, flight, or freeze. These are normal responses to acute or short-term stresses.

Chronic stress, however, is another beast. Chronic stress is when your body becomes constantly vigilant—as though it is always on the lookout for bears. On your morning commute, in the grocery store, as you go about your daily activities.

Let me make a distinction here. Stress is not an "event" that happens to you. It's your body's response to that event. It's an *internal* process. The events that trigger a stress response in your body are called stressors or demands. Those are external things. And sorry, ladies, but those demands are not going away. You will continue to have demands and stressors, and no amount of beach vacations or hot baths, or meditation will magically take them away.

The big problem with chronic stress is that, left unchecked, it can lead to burnout. Burnout is the equivalent of "end-organ failure." Think of stress, chronic stress, and burnout in terms of a continuum. Here's an example of a stress-to-burnout continuum related to your heart. Acute (healthy) stress is when your heart pumps harder while you exercise. After exercise, your heart returns to its normal resting level of pumping function.

But with chronic (unhealthy) stress, the heart continues to pump blood harder than necessary because the brain misinterprets the signals it's receiving, and it thinks you are exercising all day long as you go about your normal daily activities. Essentially, your heart functions in overdrive. Over time, the pumping function can weaken or wear out, and the heart is no longer the effective pump it used to be. Parts of the pump may break down and result in heart failure. This heart failure is the end-organ failure.

This is, of course, a gross oversimplification and not entirely accurate, but it's an effective illustration of the continuum from normal function to dysfunction to failure.

Now instead of the heart, take that same concept but substitute the adrenal glands. The adrenal glands are a pair of small triangle-shaped glands that sit on top of the kidneys and produce many of the hormones involved in the stress response, including cortisol and adrenaline.

The adrenal glands respond to stress signals by pumping out stress hormones so your body can respond to the threat (bear) or perceived threat (rush hour traffic, looming project deadlines at work, kids fighting in the next room). But when the brain misinterprets your chronic daily stressors as a bear chasing you, the adrenals pump out their stress hormones until they reach a point of dysfunction and potentially end-organ failure.

This is often referred to as adrenal fatigue or hypothalamic-pituitary-adrenal axis (HPA) dysfunction, named for the brain regions that are misfiring the signals to the adrenals.

You may be at the stage of dysfunction in the *stress -> chronic stress -> burnout continuum* and not even realize it. If you're like me, you don't look for the signs—or you ignore the signs—and you may be in end-organ failure (burnout) before you even know what hit you.

Through intentional habit transformation, you can alter how your body responds to stressful events.

But here's where you have control. You get to decide. You can alter the way your body responds to those stressors or demands. This is called stress resilience.

As defined by the Merriam-Webster dictionary, resilience is "(1) the capability of a strained body to recover its size and shape after deformation caused especially by compressive stress or (2) an ability to recover from or adjust easily to misfortune or change."

So stress resilience is your body's ability to bounce back after exposure to stress, whether that is a single major stressful event—think a wedding or moving—or all the daily demands that create compounding stress in the body.

Another concept related to stress resilience is adaptation energy. Think of your body's energy balance as a car battery. Your daily demands create stress that drains your battery. Adaptation energy is the *counter energy* to stress. This is what recharges your battery.

According to The Oxford Dictionary of Sports Science & Medicine, adaptation energy is "a hypothetical measure of an individual's capacity to resist stress. Each person is believed to have a finite amount of adaptation energy, which is used to cope with different types of stress. Energy expended to cope with one type of stress, such as staying up late, results in less being available for other stresses, such as training. When adaptation energy is low, a person is more likely to suffer from stress-related diseases and conditions known as burnout and rundown."

Adaptation energy is the counter energy to stress.

Here's one more thing to note. Many of my conventional medical colleagues fail to acknowledge the existence of adrenal fatigue or HPA dysfunction as a medical condition. If you find yourself in a conversation with your doctor and they tell you there's no such thing as adrenal fatigue, thank them for their opinion and find yourself a Functional Medicine doctor, preferably one with a traditional medical background as well—MD or DO.

Functional medicine doctors work with patients to find the *root cause* of chronic disease and dysfunction rather than simply treating the symptoms. If you are not familiar with functional medicine, I have included the following definition from The Institute For Functional Medicine. "The Functional Medicine model is an individualized, patient-centered, science-based approach that empowers patients and practitioners to work together to address the underlying causes of disease and promote optimal wellness. It requires a detailed understanding of each patient's genetic, biochemical, and lifestyle factors and leverages that data to direct personalized treatment plans that lead to improved patient outcomes. By addressing the root cause rather than symptoms, practitioners become oriented to identifying the complexity of the disease. They may find one condition has many different causes, and, likewise, one cause may result in many different conditions. As a result, Functional Medicine treatment targets the specific manifestations of disease in each individual." You can find more about Functional Medicine at www.ifm.org.

Moving forward, when I use the term stress in this book, I am referring to chronic or unhealthy stress. However, it's essential to understand that acute/short-term/healthy stress plays an important role in your health and safety.

As you evaluate the stressors in your life, think of them from the perspectives of your different Fields of Play. *Field of Play* is a concept described by author, entrepreneur, and peak performance coach Todd Herman in his book *The Alter Ego Effect*.

He describes Fields of Play as the different people, places, and things we interact with and the expectations that go along with those roles. You perform on multiple Fields of Play at any given point in your life. You may interact on one Field of Play as a parent, another as an employee or boss or business owner, a third as a coach for your kid's sports team, etcetera.

The concept of Field of Play is important to understand as we move forward because each Field of Play will come with its own set of demands or stressors, and you'll want to design a game plan to address and balance the needs of your competing Fields of Play. Don't worry, stay with me. It's simpler than it sounds!

Among other things, this book will teach you how to develop stress resilience. Stress resilience is so much more than using stress management tools or techniques in the usual sense.

How you feed your brain, how you move your body, how well you recover through rest and sleep are all very much part of developing stress resilience. And, in my experience, a more tangible place to start. So we'll dig into the basics of eating to fuel your brain, moving your body to support and nourish your brain, and restoring your brain and body through rest and restorative sleep. Following the simple principles outlined in the next chapters will help you start feeling better quickly so you can continue your journey to tame the stress monster.

But first, you have to admit you have a problem.

If you still need convincing that chronic stress is a problem in your life, you can use the reflection space in *Next Steps* to help you evaluate the stressors in your Fields of Play. If you're already on board and know that you need to make some changes now—let's face it, part of you already knew there was a problem, or you wouldn't have picked up this book—you can jump right into the next chapter on the care and feeding of a better brain.

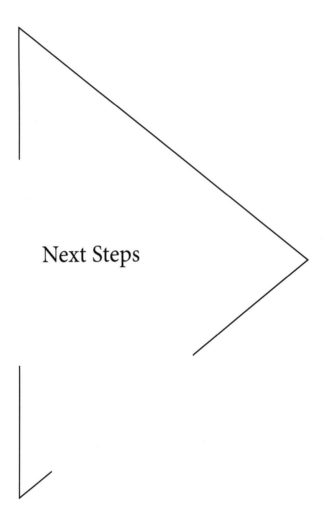

Next Steps

Write down some thoughts about how stress affects your life.

....

....

....

....

....

....

....

....

....

....

....

....

....

....

....

....

....

....

....

....

....

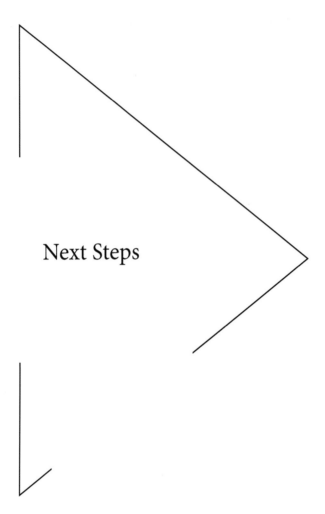

Next Steps

List your three main Fields of Play and the top stressors or demands related to each one. Fields of Play can be general—work, home, friendships. Or they can be specific—wife, mother, employee, manager, coworker, roles in community or professional associations, and so on. This list will come in handy in later chapters.

Field of Play	Stressors
1.	....
2.	....
3.	....

Part Two:
Master the Fundamentals:
Eat, Move, Sleep

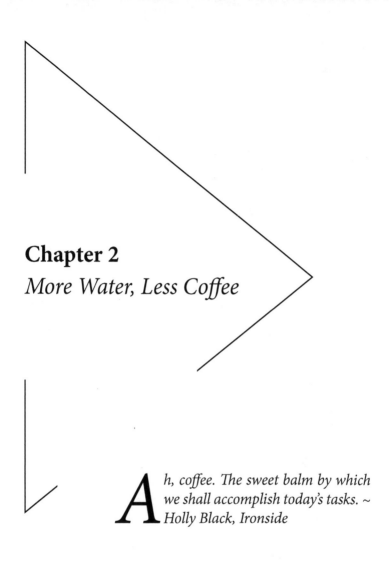

Chapter 2
More Water, Less Coffee

*A*h, coffee. The sweet balm by which we shall accomplish today's tasks. ~ Holly Black, Ironside

My adventures in nutrition—or should I say misadventures—started with a quest to cure my adult acne. Yep, vanity made me do it. I had perfectly clear skin as a teenager, and it wasn't until my late twenties and early thirties that I began struggling with acne. After failing the usual topical and prescription regimens, I went on a quest to eliminate dietary triggers.

This sent me down many different pathways, and I dabbled with various eating styles, including vegetarian, paleo, wheat-free, dairy-free, and numerous others. It wasn't until I got over my addiction to sugar and got my blood sugar under control by incorporating healthy fats back into my diet that my skin finally settled down. And when I eventually got my stress under control, that was where the magic happened. But we'll get to that later. First things first.

Why is nutrition important? You are what you eat, for one thing. What you eat and drink *literally* becomes the building blocks of every cell in your body and brain. If you eat crap, then your cells are made of low-quality materials. If you want your brain and body to perform well, you need to nourish them well. Garbage in, garbage out. Need I say more?

Now I will say upfront that reams of confusing and often contradictory information are available out there about what's good for you and what isn't. Is coffee a superfood or a toxin? What about wine? Chocolate, grains, dairy? What the heck am I supposed to eat?

The answer is—it depends. The best eating plan for *you* considers your genetic variability, preferences, allergies or intolerances, and so on. Your goal is to find the food that fuels and energizes you, and not in a jacked-up sugar or caffeinated way. Rather than following the latest food fad or celebrity diet plan—yep, been there, done that—listen to your body. Notice how you feel when you eat a certain way. Make small adjustments rather than rapid shifts. In other words, be patient and open to the idea of trial and error.

However, a few basic principles can be applied across the board, and that's where we'll start. My mantra is "keep it simple," so let's keep it *simple*.

Principle #1

My number one strategy to level up your approach to healthy eating is to *add before you subtract.*

If you start by subtracting, *depriving* yourself of the things you love, your new habits are less likely to stick. Adding healthy habits first, without focusing on eliminating the unhealthy ones, helps you start to see yourself as someone who makes better food choices. These incremental changes not only build momentum but also help you see yourself as a healthy eater. Once you start seeing the changes that eating better makes in your life—how your mood improves, how your body feels, how you think more clearly—you'll likely want to compound your successes by starting to reduce or remove the less healthy eating habits.

Principle #2

While *add before you subtract* is the most important

strategy to start with, the most crucial nutrient to focus on adding, in the beginning, is water.

Water is critical to every bodily function. Your body is composed of about 60% percent water, and your brain is made of 80% water. The importance of water and proper hydration was actually something I didn't buy into until more recently, but it has made such a substantial shift that I am now a hydration evangelist.

For an average healthy person with a moderate activity level, aim to drink half of your body weight in ounces of water daily. So if you weigh 150 pounds, you'll want to aim for drinking 75 ounces of water daily. This is a baseline and ballpark amount. If you exercise vigorously and sweat excessively, you will require more.

Now, I know what your next question is, and no, coffee does not count! Neither do other beverages, including tea, soda, fruit juices, or alcohol.

When I first implemented this strategy, I was shocked to realize how little water I actually drank. It turns out I'd only drink a little water with my meals. I generally sipped on a big cup of coffee throughout the morning and another cup of coffee or tea throughout the afternoon.

Now I start my day with a large glass of water before my morning coffee or breakfast. After I finish my one cup of morning coffee, I drink two more large glasses of water before lunch. I do the same between lunch and dinner. This has been an easy and effective way for me to get in all my hydration needs with a huge bonus of keeping me from getting hungry between meals.

Calculate your target water intake goal and make a

plan for getting this in throughout the day. If you don't work from home or an office with a ready supply of good drinking water, plan ahead and bring your own in a glass or stainless steel water bottle.

Principle #3

Eat real, whole foods whenever possible. Try to focus your nutritional choices on eating whole unprocessed or minimally processed foods as much as possible. A dietary pattern focused on eating whole fruits and vegetables, minimally processed meat, poultry and seafood, and whole grains (if you tolerate them and choose to eat them) contains the macronutrients, micronutrients, and fiber needed for a healthy brain and body.

Quality. Buy the highest quality food you can afford. Quality factors to consider include buying organic fruits and vegetables when possible to ensure you're getting the lowest possible exposure to toxic pesticides and herbicides. Local produce from farmers' markets is typically much fresher than what you can find in supermarkets, equating to better nutrient density.

Quality proteins include animals raised in natural environments—think grass-fed, pastured, wild—without antibiotics or synthetic hormones, who are treated humanely and fed their natural diets. Avoid ultra-processed junk food and traditional fast food as these are loaded with trans fats and artificial ingredients such as dyes, flavorings, and preservatives. Thankfully, reasonable alternatives for take-out are available these days.

Fiber is your friend. Fiber keeps the "pipes" clean,

and it helps you feel full and feeds the good bacteria in your gut. I consider this Principle 3.1 because if you are sticking with a predominantly whole food diet, you will have a much easier time getting adequate daily fiber. On days—or let's be honest, weeks—when your dietary choices fall short, you can add a fiber supplement to your coffee, tea, or food.

Principle #4

Mind your macros. I borrowed this phrase from nutritionist and best-selling author Shawn Stevenson. The word macros refers to macronutrients, meaning protein, fat, and carbohydrates.

The mind your macros approach means being mindful of what *balance* of protein to fat to carbs you choose for each meal and for your diet overall. Again, ideal macronutrient ratios vary by individual, but a few higher-level concepts apply pretty universally.

Most people will thrive on a balance of healthy fats, high-quality proteins, and smart carbs at each meal, with the ratio varying from person to person. Adding healthy fats into my diet was key to balancing my blood sugar and my energy levels. It's amazing what healthy fats can do to eliminate hangry from your life! Healthy fats include avocado, nuts, coconut, and extra virgin olive oil, to name a few of my daily staples.

Clean proteins include grass-fed beef, pastured chicken and eggs, and wild-caught fish. Of course, if you are vegetarian, you'll find plenty of good options for getting your protein intake as well.

Smart carbs are fruits and vegetables higher on the nutrient scale and lower on the glycemic scale. Focus on leafy greens and cruciferous vegetables and eat fewer starchy vegetables such as beets, potatoes, and squash.

I've never been a fan of counting calories or even counting macros. Just be mindful of the *balance* of food on your plate each meal. Those of us with overachiever mentalities and perfectionist tendencies can really go overboard with counting and "failing" when we don't hit the "right" numbers. Find the balance of healthy fats, clean protein, and smart carbs that fuels your body best and allows your body and brain to thrive.

Alcohol is not a superfood; it's a toxin to your brain.

You may be surprised to hear that alcohol is also considered a macronutrient. This has more to do with how the body breaks down and uses alcohol from a metabolic standpoint, and not at all about it being a nutrient or nutritious. If you choose to drink, be mindful of your alcohol consumption volume and frequency. Consider if it aligns with your overall health goals. Personally, I still enjoy a glass of wine or a cocktail with friends, but I generally limit that to once a week with a two-drink maximum. We'll discuss a little more about alcohol in the chapter on sleep, but spoiler alert, it's a sleep saboteur.

Principle #5

Step away from the sugar. Yes, you heard me correctly.

An occasional sweet treat or dessert is fine, especially if part of a meaningful celebration—like a birthday or anniversary—or paired with good conversation and good friends. I'm sure you know your nightly Ben & Jerry's habit is less than ideal, but most people underestimate the depths of their sugar habit.

And please, please stop *drinking* your sugar. Your daily grande mocha latte habit is a sugar bomb that is doing you no favors. Sugar hijacks your brain—it's highly addictive, acting on the brain's addiction center called the nucleus accumbens. It increases inflammation, feeds cancer cells, and causes rapid aging and wrinkles. Yep, sugar causes rapid aging and wrinkles. Do I have your attention now?

Sugar and other simple carbs—think bread and pasta—triggers a significant insulin response which drives sugar into your cells, storing it as fat, which causes your blood sugar level to dive. In turn, this triggers hunger and the hangry feeling I know you're familiar with. Adding healthy fats and clean protein to every meal helps blunt the insulin response and gives you more stable blood sugar levels. So no sugar or simple carbs = no blood sugar rollercoaster = no hangry. Got it?

Unfortunately, artificial sweeteners such as aspartame, saccharin, and sucralose (Splenda) come with their own set of problems. These chemicals may be calorie-free but come with risk profiles that disrupt your gut microbiome and can cause cancer, as shown in animal studies. They can also spike your blood sugar—yep, you read that right—triggering the insulin response, and strongly stimulate the addiction centers in the brain.

Ditch sugar and artificial sweeteners for *just two weeks*, and you won't even miss it— especially if you replace it with healthy fats which are satisfying and more filling.

You'll be amazed at the flavor and sweetness of whole natural fruit once you cut the processed stuff out of your diet. For tasty and healthy alternatives to putting sugar in your coffee, try a splash of heavy cream, canned coconut milk or coconut cream, or a mix of butter and coconut oil or MCT oil blended into your java. Don't knock it till you try it!

Principle #6
Avoid always-never thinking when it comes to food.

Eliminating entire classes of foods, which may create some short-term results for some individuals, is a surefire road to imbalances and more serious problems when continued over the long term. Do your best to keep your perfectionist tendencies check and avoid believing or behaving as if you have to eat perfectly 100% of the time.

Orthorexia is a condition originally described by Steven Bratman, MD, in 1996 and is characterized by an *unhealthy focus* on eating healthily. Practice moderation rather than pursuing perfection. Is the "cost" of indulging in a piece of birthday cake today really of more concern to you than celebrating your five-year-olds birthday?

Principle #7

Remember Grandma's rules. Rethink *how* you eat. Above and beyond what you eat, it's important to think about how you eat. This principle contains two important objectives.

One is the concept of mindful eating. This includes sitting down while you eat and eliminating other distractions. And yes, that means your phone. Notice the color, taste, aroma, texture, and flavor of what you're eating. Food is meant to be enjoyed, so savor your meals. And for goodness sake, chew your food.

A major source of gastrointestinal issues these days is improper digestion, and digestion begins in the mouth. Taking the time to chew each bite of food until it's essentially liquid in the mouth and easy to swallow will pay dividends in terms of reducing gastrointestinal discomfort and improving nutrient absorption.

Another important concept is paying attention to *when* you eat. If you're fueling yourself properly—see Principle #4 above—at mealtimes, you should not need to snack throughout the day. Frequent grazing throughout the day wreaks havoc on your stress hormones and the hormones that regulate your blood sugar.

Eating late at night is also a recipe for disaster. Not only will this interfere with your sleep quality, but studies show that late-night grazers weigh more than those who finish their last meal several hours before bedtime. Aim for a minimum of two to three hours between your last meal and hitting the hay. Assuming you're getting a healthy amount of sleep—seven to eight hours—avoiding food three hours before bed gives your body and your digestive system twelve-plus hours without food, depending on the timing of your next meal. This concept has recently been labeled intermittent fasting, time-restricted eating, or circadian fasting, but my grandma would have called this *not snacking*.

- Add before you subtract
- Water is a critical nutrient
- Eat real, whole foods
- Mind your macros
- Ditch the sugar and artificial sweeteners
- Avoid always-never thinking
- Remember Grandma's rules

How you choose to fuel your body and brain directly correlates to how well it performs for you day in and day out. Make some simple changes, and you'll quickly notice a difference in how you feel. Remember, *add before you subtract*. The biggest game-changers for me were adding healthy fats at every meal, drinking a lot more water throughout the day, and adding more green leafy veggies.

Now that you have the Nutrition 101 fundamentals, our next stop is exercise, the fountain of youth!

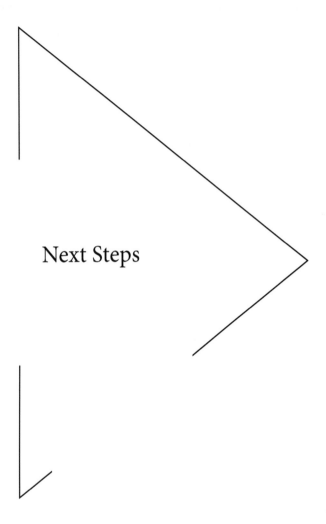

Next Steps

What small steps can you take *today* to start moving the needle toward better energy levels?

....
....
....
....
....
....
....

How much water are you currently drinking daily?

....
....
....
....
....
....
....

Based on the guidelines outlined in this chapter, how many ounces of water per day is your target?

....
....
....
....
....
....

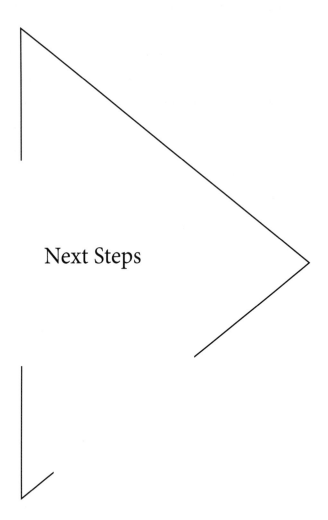

Next Steps

What steps can you take to increase your daily water intake?

....

....

....

....

....

....

....

....

....

....

Which healthy fats can you add at each meal to help stabilize your blood sugar levels?

....

....

....

....

....

....

....

....

....

....

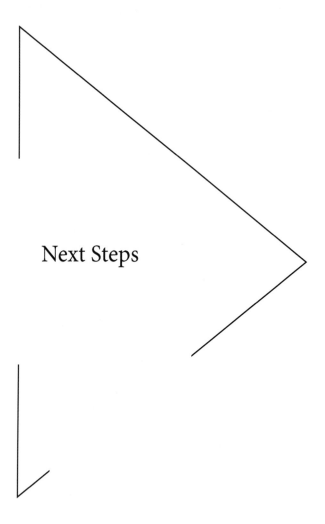

Next Steps

Think about your overall eating and drinking habits in relation to the seven principles.

What are you doing well?

....
....
....
....
....
....
....
....
....
....

Which areas could use improvement?

....
....
....
....
....
....
....
....
....
....

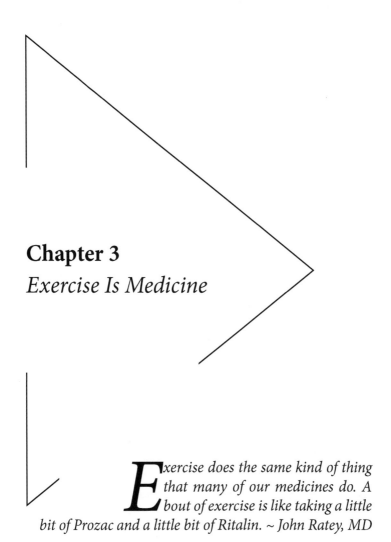

Chapter 3
Exercise Is Medicine

*E*xercise does the same kind of thing
that many of our medicines do. A
bout of exercise is like taking a little
bit of Prozac and a little bit of Ritalin. ~ John Ratey, MD

I grew up playing sports and always considered myself an athlete, but I *hated* to run. I remember fudging the weekly running log we had to submit during summer conditioning for the high school gymnastics team— sorry, Coach Bobbi!

I didn't develop an affinity for running until my mid-thirties. I started running short distances with a friend, and we subsequently joined a larger running group. It was a great stress release and an opportunity for social connection. They became my "people." I would get up at 4:30 am, run with the group, come home, get ready for work and get the kids off to school. I felt great physically, connected with friends I enjoyed, and felt very productive—getting my workout in before my family even woke up in the morning. And then, being someone who doesn't do moderation very well, I was hooked, and in a short time, I was running longer and longer distances, completing several half marathons.

Anyone who's been a runner knows that adding mileage too quickly is a recipe for disaster. So what happened? I got injured, of course. First, there was a hamstring tear. I rehabbed from that injury and went back to running. Then a year or so later, while in the home stretch of training for my first full marathon, I developed a compression fracture in my hip during an eighteen-mile run. I quit running immediately after that happened, but I limped around on it for a full month before I bothered to get it checked out. Did I mention that doctors are the worst patients? I struggled with moderation and balance, both within my running habit and within my life overall.

Exercise is an antidote for much of what ails us in the western world. The benefits of exercise are far-reaching, from improving metabolism, improving heart health, improving brain health, improving bone density, and improving a sense of well-being and body confidence.

Exercise improves your sleep and improves sexual health. It lowers inflammation in the body—however, extreme sports such as marathon running can actually cause damage to DNA from oxidative stress. On a physiologic level, exercise improves blood flow, oxygen, and blood glucose levels. It increases DNA repair and protects against free radicals. It lowers blood sugar and increases insulin sensitivity.

Exercise lowers the risk of dementia and improves cognition and psychological well-being. It increases certain neurotransmitters and upregulates brain-derived neurotrophic factor (BDNF). BDNF promotes the survival of nerve cells and also promotes neurogenesis, which is the process of growing new brain cells. And these new brain cells help modulate the stress response.

As Dr. John Ratey notes, "The fitter you are, the more stress it takes to get you stressed." This is related to the concept of adaptation energy that we discussed in Chapter 1. And in addition to the neurogenesis-related stress modulation, exercise also physically helps burn off stress. Exercise is a mood booster, touted as being the equivalent of a little bit of Prozac and a little bit of Ritalin, without the side effects. Who wouldn't want that?

The fitter you are, the more stress it takes to get you stressed.

Most people would agree that exercise is good, but the concepts of balance and moderation are critical. Let's start with thinking about the activity continuum from being sedentary to being very active. Being sedentary is clearly bad for your health. Sitting is the new smoking, right? The goal is to be much more active throughout the day. It's common to hear people shooting for a target of 7000 to 10,000 steps per day. There's no magic number here, but generally, remaining active throughout the day rather than sitting all day is the goal. However, in this knowledge-worker economy, many of us sit through the majority of our workdays.

Exercise is different from physical activity. Exercise is generally thought of as taking a specified amount of time to engage in a physical fitness activity. This can be anything from playing tennis to brisk walking to working out in the gym. Exercise is good and important for optimal physical and psychological health, but exercise is not the same thing as activity on the sedentary-activity spectrum.

You can work out hard for 30 minutes every day, but if you sit on your rear the rest of the day, you're still at risk from a sedentary lifestyle. So shoot for both—an active lifestyle *and* a regular exercise routine. You don't have to become a fitness fanatic. Aiming for 7000+ steps per day—roughly the equivalent of walking two and a half to three miles—and three to four bouts of exercise per week is plenty of activity and exercise to support a healthy mind and body.

You can incorporate exercise into your life in a wide variety of ways. Team sports combine the benefits of physical fitness with the benefits of social connection, and they use the cognitive skills required to perform complex dynamic activities. Aerobic exercise such as brisk walking, running, or swimming benefits your heart and your brain. Strength training helps build muscle strength, bone strength, and brain strength. Exercises incorporating flexibility, balance, and coordination provide benefits that complement strength training and aerobic exercise. High-intensity interval training (HIIT) has grown in popularity and provides combined aerobic and strength training benefits. Mind-body exercises such as yoga, tai chi, or Pilates, which combine physical movement with breathwork and mindfulness, provide both physical and psychological benefits as well.

If you struggle with moderation—like me—exercise can be a double-edged sword. Exercise is good, but too much can cause problems. Over-exercising can worsen the physical effects of stress and burnout on your body. Shoot for a regular weekly exercise program that combines aerobic exercise and strength training at a minimum. Again, thirty to forty-five minutes of aerobic exercise three to five days per week and thirty minutes of strength training twice a week is all you need for optimizing your physical and mental health.

When you're ready to add more, flexibility, balance,

and coordination activities could be performed as separate workouts or simply incorporated into your routine strength training or aerobic workouts. If you're not exercising at all right now, *any* amount of exercise you add is a step in the right direction, and you will start seeing benefits within just a few weeks.

Exercise makes you smarter, happier, and less stressed—and grows new brain cells! What are you waiting for? If you're eager to learn more about exercise, I highly recommend checking out the TED Talk by Dr. Wendy Suzuki on the *Brain Changing Benefits of Exercise* or check out the recommended reading list on the book resources webpage.

My top three tips on exercise to get you started are— move more, sit less, and practice variety and moderation.

Exercise makes you smarter, happier, and less stressed.

You have now mastered the first two fundamentals of a healthier life—eating and moving. In the final chapter in this fundamentals section, we'll tackle sleep. Dig right in to see how you can make sleep your new superpower!

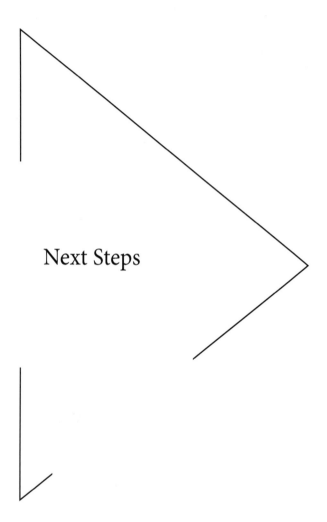

Next Steps

Evaluate your current exercise routine and level of activity.

Physical activity:

Do you sit most of the day for work?

....

....

....

If so, do you take regular stretch breaks or walking breaks throughout the day?

....

....

....

If you use a device or app to count your steps, what's your average daily step count?

....

....

....

If walking is part of your daily routine, what distance miles or time in minutes do you usually walk?

....

....

....

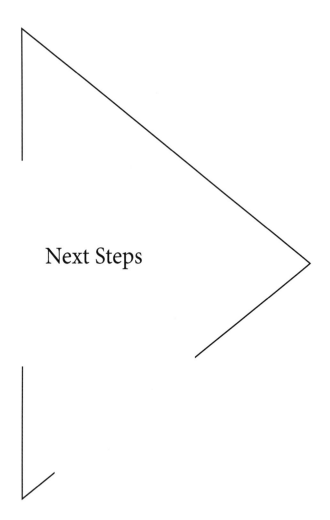

Next Steps

Exercise:

Days per week ....

....

....

....

Time spent per day ....

....

....

....

Aerobic exercise ....

....

....

....

....

Strength training ....

....

....

....

....

Other ....

....

....

....

....

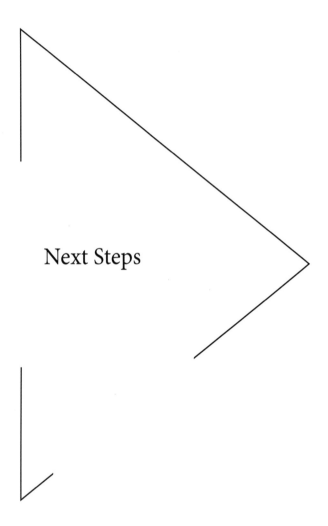

Next Steps

What are you doing well?

....

....

....

....

....

....

Where do you need to improve?

....

....

....

....

....

....

What small steps can you take today to start moving the needle toward better physical activity levels?

....

....

....

....

....

....

....

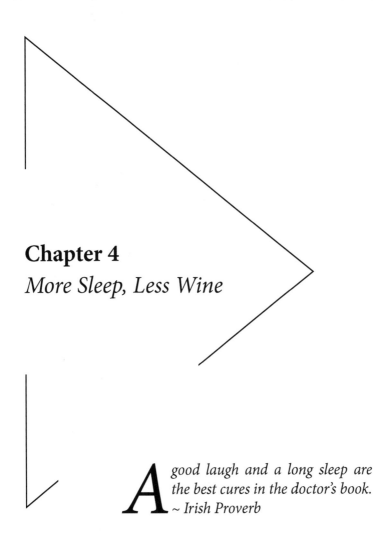

Chapter 4
More Sleep, Less Wine

A *good laugh and a long sleep are
the best cures in the doctor's book.*
~ Irish Proverb

Sleep was my superpower...until it wasn't. I could sleep anytime, anywhere. On the couch, on the floor, in a lecture hall. And at night, I could literally fall asleep in under two minutes. It drove my husband crazy, as he often struggled to fall asleep at night. I was also a champion napper, and I could take two-hour naps on the weekends given the (rare) opportunity. What I didn't realize was that I could fall asleep literally anywhere and in an instant because I was *overtired*. I was not getting enough sleep. Or at least not enough restorative sleep.

Sleep plays a critical role in the function of your brain and body. Sleep helps you recover from the demands of the day, both physical and mental, and helps prepare you to meet the demands of the following day. The science of recovery is exploding in areas like sports performance. Train hard, yes, but if you don't spend equal effort on your recovery, your training efforts are wasted. Sleep is a critical component of athletic recovery, but it is also a critical component of recovery for us mere mortals.

Superstar athletes like LeBron James are said to sleep ten to twelve hours each night routinely. LeBron has one job—to play basketball at the elite professional level. And while your day job might not be quite as demanding as LeBron's, I'm betting you have two or more jobs you are trying to balance—working professional, mom, and whatever else you've got on your plate that you may be unpaid but is still part of your unofficial job duties. So if you want to excel at your job and show up for your kids and your family as your best self, take a cue from The King and prioritize sleep as part of your recovery plan.

Quantity

Most people need seven to nine hours of sleep at night to function optimally. The two biggest objections to this I hear are, "I only need six hours of sleep," and "I don't have time to sleep that much." While there may be a few genetic superheroes out there who truly can thrive on six hours of sleep or less, most of us are just kidding ourselves that we don't need that much sleep.

Are you really doing "fine" on six hours of sleep? Really? Or are you sliding by on six hours of sleep … for now? Are you using caffeine to wake up in the morning? And then again, when the afternoon slump hits? Caffeine, by the way, does not give you energy. It blocks the receptors in your brain that tell you that you're tired. If you are using caffeine as a crutch to get through your days, you're not getting adequate sleep, despite what you're trying to tell yourself.

Now, let's tackle the "I don't have time" excuse. If you are a single mom working multiple jobs to pay the bills and support your family, this may be a legitimate concern, but if that doesn't describe you and you are still telling yourself, "I don't have time to sleep more," let's do a reality check. Do a time audit.

For three days, write down how you spend every hour of the day. Be honest. You're the only one who is going to see this. Check the screen time use on your phone. Calculate how many hours a day you spend watching TV, surfing the internet, and scrolling on your phone. I'm confident that you can find time to sleep more. It's a matter of priorities. Choose to prioritize your health over your Instagram Stories.

Quality

Sleep quality matters, too. If you crash in bed from exhaustion and wake up tired seven to eight hours later, you are suffering from sleep quality issues. Let me give you a super brief primer on sleep. Your body goes through sleep cycles at night, each approximately ninety minutes long, and you go through four to six of these cycles nightly. The cycles consist of light sleep, deep sleep, and REM (rapid eye movement) sleep.

During light sleep, you are more alert and are fairly easily awoken by sounds or even just your partner moving in bed. Deep sleep is the restorative phase of sleep during which hormones are released, and the body and brain go into repair mode. REM sleep is when dreaming occurs, and your mind is quite active. The stages of deep sleep and REM sleep are the most restorative phases and most affected by sleep thieves. What are sleep thieves? I'm glad you asked!

Sleep Thieves

Sleep thieves are the things you do or don't do that steal precious restorative Z's from your night's sleep. The most common sleep thieves are caffeine, alcohol, and light.

Avoid caffeine after 2 pm. The half-life of caffeine is six hours, meaning that if you drink a cup of coffee containing 200mg of caffeine at 2 pm, you will still have 100mg of caffeine in your bloodstream six hours later at 8 pm. And if you've been taking in a constant infusion of caffeine from 7 am to 2 pm, 3 pm, or later, you've got a ton of caffeine coursing through your veins when you're ready to hit the hay. And while you may not be able to feel the effects of the caffeine because you feel tired and ready to sleep, the caffeine will still interfere with getting that deep restorative sleep. Don't forget that coffee is not the only caffeinated culprit. Tea, including black and green varieties, also contains caffeine, albeit in lesser concentrations.

Next, let's tackle alcohol. Alcohol is a depressant, which means it helps you feel calm and sleepy, but it's a terrible nightcap! While it may help you fall asleep, once it wears off, there is a rebound effect, and you will often wake in the middle of the night and have trouble getting back to sleep. Even if it doesn't fully wake you up, it keeps your body from getting into the deep restorative sleep phases. Do yourself a favor and enjoy your glass of wine earlier in the evening, after you get home from work or with dinner. This will make it much less likely to negatively impact your sleep.

The last major sleep thief we'll talk about is light. When it comes to sleep, light, especially blue light, is a double edge sword. We actually need to be exposed to light early in the morning, when the sun rises, to keep our circadian rhythms finely tuned. After the sun goes down, exposure to artificial light wreaks havoc on our natural circadian rhythms, so early morning natural light exposure helps keep things in check.

Exposure to artificial light after dark tricks our brains into thinking it's still daytime and prevents the secretion of melatonin, which is the master sleep hormone. Blue light can especially interfere with melatonin production, and this can come from the lighting in our home and from our TV, computer, and phone screens. You can hack this sleep thief by using some of the commonly available blue light blocking tools and gadgets, which range from glasses with blue-blocking lenses to filters on your devices that cut down on the blue light waves emitted by the devices, to light bulbs that are red or amber-hued.

Dimming your overhead lights or using accessory lighting such as lamps with the warmer wavelengths after dark can help support natural melatonin production, which in turn will support better sleep.

Other common sleep thieves include eating too late or drinking too many fluids in the evening. Eating too late causes your body to focus on digestion rather than recovery, and having to wake in the middle of the night to pee is disruptive to sleep for obvious reasons.

Common Sleep Thieves:
- Caffeine
- Alcohol
- Late meals
- Artificial light after dark
- Screen time too close to bedtime
- Too much fluid in the evening

Sleep Enhancers
The good news is that, in addition to minimizing sleep thieves, there are also things you can add to your environment or bedtime routine to improve your sleep. I

call these sleep enhancers.

If you want better sleep, your best friend is a cool, dark, and quiet bedroom. And by dark, I mean blackout dark. Blackout curtains are available at all price points and are a highly valuable investment in your health and sanity. Blackout dark also means eliminating bright lights from alarm clocks or other digital devices. If your alarm clock has a dimmer switch, turn it all the way down to the lowest setting. Quiet means turn off all notifications on your devices. If you live in a city with traffic or other outside noises to contend with, a heavier fabric curtain can help dampen outside noise and ensure a quieter night's sleep.

A good bedtime routine can add to your sleep quality as well. Keeping a consistent daily bedtime—that varies only within one hour—and sleep schedule, including weekends, is beneficial. In addition, getting deep sleep, particularly during the hours of 10 pm-2 am, is optimal for hormone secretion and recovery.

Pre-sleep rituals such as a bath or shower, soothing music, or reading a non-digital book can help promote sleep. But getting a good night's sleep really starts earlier in the day. Daily exercise and meditation both promote restful sleep, but avoid vigorous exercise too close to bedtime. If you really want to boost your sleep, consider implementing a "digital sunset" where you put your devices to bed for the night when the sun goes down. That means TV, computers, and phones. That can be pretty tough, to say the least, and sometimes impractical. But if you need to reboot your sleep, commit to a digital sunset for just two weeks, and you'll see what a difference it makes, especially in getting more deep restorative sleep.

Personally, I aim for an 8 pm cutoff for devices. On nights where I stay on my computer or phone later than that, I can see the difference in my deep sleep cycles on my Oura ring sleep app. Remember, it's the deep sleep cycles that allow your brain to transfer learning and memories into long-term storage, and also when the brain clears out the metabolic waste products that have accumulated during the day. If your brain doesn't have the opportunity to take out the trash, you're not going to be able to function at your best.

Sleep Enhancers:
- Blackout dark room
- Cool room
- Quiet
- Digital sunset
- No food or alcohol three hours before bedtime
- No caffeine after 2 pm
- Consistent bedtime

Here's a word of caution on sleeping pills. Most often, these drugs will help you fall asleep but don't always help you stay asleep, nor do they help you achieve deep restorative sleep. Some are habit-forming and have disconcerting risks such as night eating or sleepwalking. Prescription and over-the-counter sleep aids are intended only for short-term use—only a few days at a time. The dietary supplement melatonin, a hormone naturally produced by your brain, appears to be a safer option for most people, but it's better not to rely on it routinely. I use it when I travel to deal with jet lag and unfamiliar and less controlled sleeping environments. Occasionally I'll use it if I have a late afternoon coffee or a glass of wine in the evening to help offset the hit to my sleep quality from alcohol or caffeine.

My top three sleep tips are empty stomach, blackout dark/cool room, and avoid sleep disruptors such as alcohol, caffeine, screen time, and blue light.

As we close out Part Two on the fundamentals and move on to focus on managing stress, I want to drive home the point that the fundamentals are just that— *fundamental* to building your stress resilience. Yes, you need to add active stress management tools. However, build your foundation by optimizing your nutrition, engaging in healthy levels of physical activity, and ensuring quality sleep. If you follow these three suggestions, you'll start from a place of health and strength as you gain greater control of your stress with additional tools. So continue to practice and improve on.

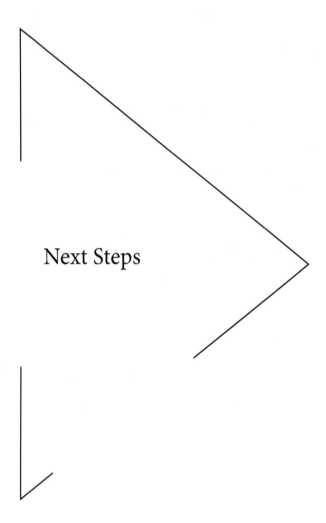

Next Steps

Evaluate your current sleep routine from the perspective of quantity, quality, and how refreshed you feel when you wake in the morning.

How many hours of sleep do you get on average?

....

....

....

Do you have trouble falling asleep?

....

....

Do you have trouble staying asleep?

....

....

Do you feel well-rested when you wake in the morning?

....

....

....

....

....

....

....

....

....

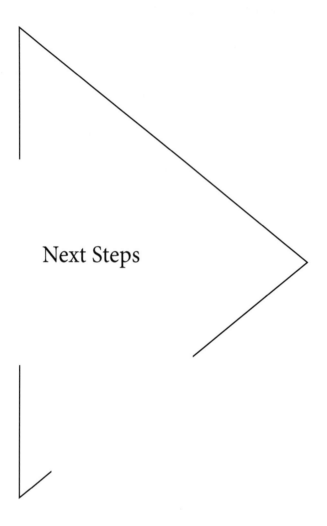

Next Steps

Review the lists of Sleep Thieves and Sleep Enhancers.

What are you doing well?

....

....

....

....

....

....

Where do you need to improve?

....

....

....

....

....

....

What small steps can you take today to start moving the needle toward more restorative sleep?

....

....

....

....

....

....

....

Part Three:
Tame the Stress Monster

Chapter 5

Stress Makes You Stupid, Sick, and Fat

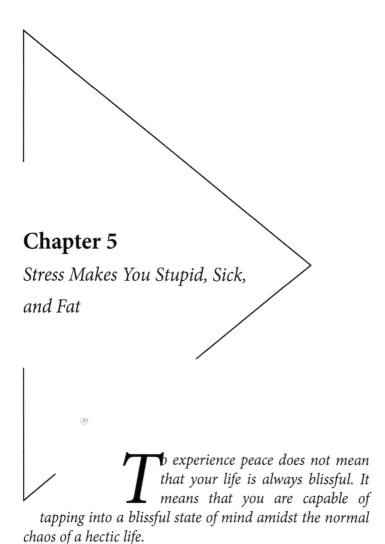

*T*o experience peace does not mean that your life is always blissful. It means that you are capable of tapping into a blissful state of mind amidst the normal chaos of a hectic life.

~ Dr. Jill Bolte Taylor

In the introduction, I shared a story about how stress made me stupid. Okay, stupid may not be the best or most appropriate word, but it got your attention, right?

Brain fog is probably a better term for what I experienced. I never really understood that term until I experienced it for myself. It wasn't that I couldn't pay attention. I had no trouble focusing on my own work product. But things were moving a mile a minute at work, and I just started having trouble keeping up with the day-to-day decisions and changes put into place by others. I couldn't remember things that I needed to remember to remain high-functioning in my work and at home. In turn, that generated fear which snowballed into the feeling of overwhelm.

Either way, I felt like my brain failed me when I needed it most. But the reality was that I had failed my brain... by years and years *and years* of neglect. In hindsight, I'm quite frankly surprised that my brain didn't check out on me sooner. I knew I was overworked and overwhelmed. But remember—I had a superpower! I was a sleep superhero, and I really thought that was enough to make up for the busyness and chaos of my perfectly crazy life.

So let's focus on how to "de-stress" and develop stress resiliency, but first, we'll review some basic concepts about how stress affects the body and brain.

- Stress is modulated by cortisol.
- Stress causes brain atrophy.
- Stress impairs your immunity.
- Stress makes you fat.

Key Concept #1
Stress is modulated by cortisol. Cortisol, one of the major stress hormones, also plays a crucial role in regulating your metabolism, blood glucose levels, blood pressure, and inflammatory and immune responses in the body.

Key Concept #2
Stress causes brain atrophy. Having persistently elevated cortisol levels related to chronic stress damages the hippocampus—one of the key brain areas involved in learning and memory—and the frontal lobe, which is responsible for higher cognitive functions, including memory, emotions, problem-solving, social interactions, and impulse control.

Key Concept #3
Stress impairs your immunity. Cortisol is essential when it comes to regulating your immune system.

When cortisol levels are too high due to chronic stress, our immune system can become hypersensitive and over-react, resulting in too much inflammation and issues such as allergies or autoimmunity.

When cortisol levels are too low—at times of adrenal fatigue and HPA axis dysfunction—the normal inflammatory response becomes weak, and the body can't mount an effective attack against infections.

What we really need is for cortisol to act like Goldilocks—not too much, not too little, but just right!

Key Concept #4

Stress makes you fat. When the stress response is activated, the body responds by releasing stored glucose into the bloodstream in preparation for fight or flight. But when we don't physically burn off that extra blood glucose, our bodies turn that into fat. And since the cells in our abdomen have a higher concentration of cortisol receptors than other parts of the body, guess where that extra fat gets stored? You got it, belly fat, courtesy of chronic stress.

So that's the bad news. What's the good news, you ask? You can reprogram your current stress response from one that constantly drains your battery and will eventually make you stupid, sick and fat, to one that keeps your battery well charged and places you on top of your game!

How do we reprogram our stress response and recharge our batteries? I'm so glad you asked! The following are samples of activities that are all effective in reducing stress. Remember, you will continue to have demands on your time and attention, but by incorporating stress-reducing actions and activities into your daily life, you can increase your adaptation energy.

Tools of the Trade

In the past three chapters, we focused on the fundamentals—healthy nutrients to fuel your brain and body, exercise and physical activity, and restorative sleep. These are the basic physiologic activities that we can optimize to become more stress-resilient. I mention them again here because they're a relatively easy place to start, and optimizing the fundamentals automatically lowers stress. It's like getting a head-start. And who doesn't want that?

The following groups of activities all work, in part, by activating the parasympathetic nervous system, the system responsible for rest and relaxation, and shutting down the sympathetic nervous system, the body's fight or flight stress response system.

The first toolset consists of *mind-body activities.* These include yoga, tai chi, and Pilates, among others. Mind-body activities incorporate movement with mindfulness and breathwork. Many current scientific studies support their effectiveness in managing stress as well as supporting positive impacts on mood, sleep, and pain.

Another group of stress-busting activities is often overlooked. I call this group connection. Social connection with friends or family, connection with nature, spending time with pets, listening to or playing music, creative endeavors you enjoy such as painting or drawing all help connect you to your inner self and are known to reduce stress levels.

My favorite stress reduction tool is laughter. There is *nothing* like a good belly laugh with friends or a while watching classic comedy to lower your stress level and instantly boost your mood—*Bridesmaids* bridal shop scene, anyone?

The next toolset to consider is *active relaxation* techniques. These include diaphragmatic (belly) breathing and other breathwork, progressive muscle relaxation, and heart-rate variability training. These are tremendous tools to help you manage day-to-day stressors. However, it is essential to practice them and hone your skills so they can be quickly and effectively deployed when your four-year-old spills red Gatorade on your white carpet.

The last toolset to discuss is *cognitive tools*. The cognitive tools group includes mindfulness, meditation, and prayer. One important thing to point out with this group is the distinction between mindfulness and meditation. These terms are often used interchangeably, but they're not the same thing.

Mindfulness requires focused attention on something—your breath, for example—and requires you to "clear your mind" and focus on that particular sensation. When—not if, because this will absolutely happen—you find your mind wandering, you are supposed to gently redirect your thoughts back to your focus. *Mindfulness as a form of meditation* is difficult and often frustrating. You cannot stop your mind from thinking any more than you can stop your heart from beating.

However, incorporating mindfulness in your daily activities is more attainable and produces positive results. For example, you can use mindfulness when you eat by paying attention to *all of your senses*. Before you take your first bite, look at your meal. Notice the colors on your plate. Notice the aroma of your food. Take a bite. Notice the temperature, texture, and flavor. Savor every bite. What do you hear? Listen for the crunch of your food or the scraping of your spoon on your plate.

Mindfulness while eating helps you slow down and focus on your meals, which improves digestion and satiety.

Meditation is another cognitive tool. A wide array of meditation forms are available, and a full explanation is outside of the scope of this book. However, if you tried meditation and it "didn't work," more likely than not, you have just not found the right type of meditation *for you.* Prayer is considered a special form of meditation and may produce similar health benefits to meditation, including psychological and biological changes in the brain and body.

Now here's where I get on my soapbox. Full disclosure: I have strong opinions about meditation. Why? Because I have tried and failed various meditation techniques. I had trouble sticking with many, and I eventually gave up because I didn't see the return on investment of my time. I tried several of the common free and paid meditation apps. But they were all mindfulness-based and required you to focus on your breathing or whatever else the audio suggested, with the intention of clearing your mind. Who can do that?

Then I came across an online meditation training program that changed *everything* for me. I signed up right before the COVID pandemic really hit and learned how to meditate in two weeks. On my own. No audio or special equipment required. Just a commitment to get my rear in the chair every day and do it. And I have succeeded in sticking with it and getting my rear in the chair to meditate—*every day* since. Why? It worked!

It worked and became a lasting habit for two reasons—

both related to the science of Behavior Design. One, because it was simple and simplicity changes behavior. Two, because it included components of emotion, and emotion helps wire in new habits quickly. These Behavior Design principles come from the research of BJ Fogg, Ph.D., the director of the Behavior Design Lab at Stanford University. More on Behavior Design and how to create habits that stick later.

But how did meditation help me? Let me state this simply—I made it through the COVID lockdown with two extra family members living with us, my husband and I both working from home, two kids doing online school and work, in an urban row house with literally zero "extra" room. And I did this without killing my husband, losing my sh**, and even more impressively, without increasing my wine intake!

What do I love about this type of meditation? Well, first, it's referred to as the "lazy man's meditation," which kind of had me at hello! And it's guilt-free because you can't "fail" or have a "bad" meditation. This style of meditation teaches that thoughts are not the enemy, you cannot stop your mind from thinking any more than you can stop your heart from beating, and there's no such thing as a good or bad meditation. It can be done anywhere in just about any comfortable sitting position; no yoga poses or special gear required.

However, you do need to learn from a trained teacher, but once you learn how to do it, it costs you nothing to practice for the rest of your life, and the returns you get are bountiful. My teacher was Emily Fletcher, founder of

Ziva Meditation, and you can find a link to her program and her book on the book resources webpage.

Meditation has well-researched, wide-ranging positive effects on your health and well-being. It lowers blood pressure, increases the production of hormones and neurotransmitters that improve your mood, reduces anxiety, improves sleep, and reduces stress. It boosts your immunity, reduces pain, and has been shown to enhance self-esteem and quality of life. It has been documented by MRI to produce measurable changes in your brain *in just eight weeks.* So you don't have to meditate for decades to reap the benefits. If you want to try meditation, learn from a teacher if you can; otherwise read a book, take an online course, or watch a few videos.

My top three stress management tips are to try out different stress resilience practices until you find one or more that you love, commit to making it part of your daily routine, and make it non-negotiable!

Clearly, I advocate using meditation as a tool to develop stress resilience and create adaptation energy. But as we outlined in the last few chapters, managing your stress isn't about having a tool you pull out only when you feel stressed. Nor is it about simply spending fifteen or thirty minutes a day to do a stress-reducing activity. This is important, vital even, but not enough.

Healthy lifestyle changes in your food choices, physical activity, and sleep are also key parts of the formula, as is learning to manage your energy. And managing your energy, as we'll discuss in the next chapter, starts with defining your priorities and creating boundaries.

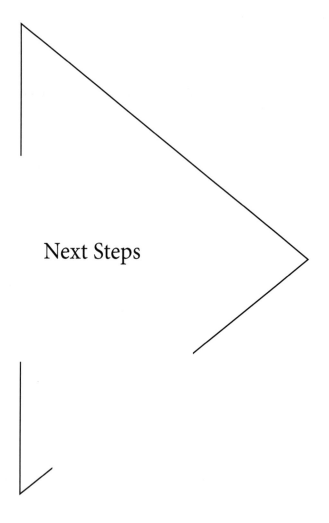

Next Steps

Evaluate your current stress resilience plan.

What are you doing well?

....
....
....
....
....
....
....
....
....
....
....

Where do you need to improve?

....
....
....
....
....
....
....
....
....
....

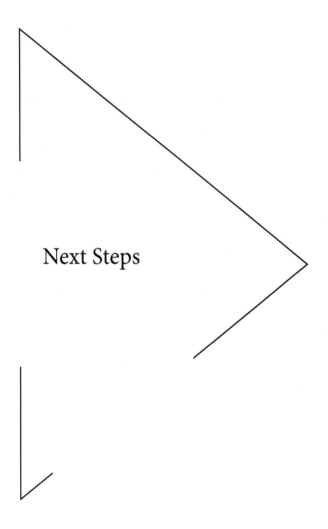

Next Steps

What small steps can you take today to start moving the needle toward better stress resilience and greater adaptation energy?

....

....

....

....

....

....

....

....

....

....

....

....

....

....

....

....

....

....

....

....

....

....

....

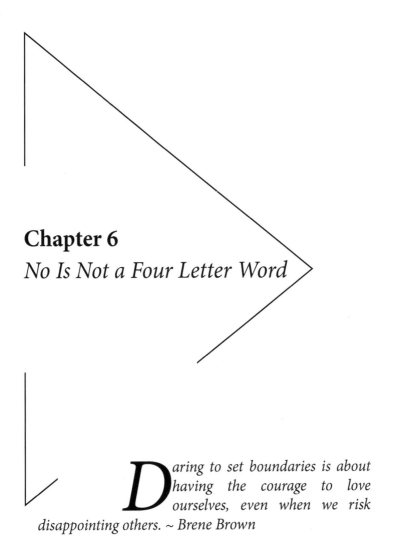

Chapter 6
No Is Not a Four Letter Word

*D*aring to set boundaries is about having the courage to love ourselves, even when we risk disappointing others. ~ Brene Brown

What I know now that I didn't realize before is that I have been driven by achievement my entire life. Being the third child of four kids in a middle-class family, achievement was an attention-getter.

Academic achievement—or musical achievement, in particular—was important in my family. But the musical gene skipped me, which was later confirmed by my 23andMe results, so academics it was! I did well in school and was always near the top of my class. I also knew from a young age that going to college was expected and that I would have to find a way to pay for that myself. Thus, I worked multiple jobs from a young age. I also knew I had to keep my grades up for scholarship opportunities and to keep my options open for getting into the colleges and programs I wanted to pursue.

I graduated from high school a year early and went straight to college. After two years of college, I entered a highly competitive physical therapy degree program. But before I graduated as a physical therapist, I had already set my sights higher; I decided to go to medical school. Four fun-filled—uh, not exactly—years later, I graduated with honors, again at the top of my class, and was accepted to my top choice for residency training. In my final year of training, I was named chief resident.

My pursuit of achievement didn't stop after I completed my training. I constantly learned new things, became a serial "intrapreneur" in my private practice, and even went back to school for a master's degree in management. In hindsight, pursuing all of these learning opportunities not only fed my drive for achievement but also helped manage burnout to some extent, as I loved learning new things.

Even so, burnout reared its head from time to time, and I changed positions a few times over the years. But even as I moved to jobs that *theoretically* should have been less stressful or less intense, I continued to seek achievement via promotions and increasing responsibility. And how did I pursue and ultimately achieve those promotions? I worked my tail off, of course, but I also never said no, which worked for the overachiever in me, but not so much for the part of me that sought balance. And sanity.

You see, my driven, Type A, overachieving self was another double-edged sword. It launched me into being a successful physician, business executive, and entrepreneur, and it led me to being overworked, overtired, overwhelmed, and burned out. Learning about boundaries and, more importantly, learning to believe I had the power to create my own boundaries was a major tipping point in my recovery.

Let's start by defining boundaries. I love the definition as described by Dr. Henry Cloud in his book *Boundaries for Leaders*. "Boundaries are what you create and what you allow. In the end, as a leader, you are always going to get a combination of two things: what you create and what you allow." Cloud also describes the central principle of boundaries as *ownership*. You have to own that you are "ridiculously in charge" of what you create and what you allow. This applies to both your work and home life. Think about it. What are you allowing to happen at work or at home that is contributing to your overwhelm? What boundaries could you put in place to reclaim control of your situation?

Boundaries are what you create and what you allow.

Why are boundaries important, especially for high achievers? First, setting clear boundaries based on your priorities allows you to manage your energy. And energy, not time, is the fundamental element of high performance. This concept of managing energy as the primary means to high performance comes from Jim Loehr and Tony Schwartz in their book, *The Power of Full Engagement*. Second, evaluating how you are spending your energy— not just your time—gives you perspective on what shifts you could make to align your energy with your priorities.

The key to success is spending your energy on things that drive results, not on busy work. Ideally, you want to focus 80% of your energy on the top 20% of high-yielding activities in your life. Again, you may want to think of this from the perspective of your different Fields of Play. Where is your energy focused? Is it aligned with your top priorities?

A couple of key concepts have helped me manage my energy. One is clarity. Clarity can mean a lot of things. In this case, I'm talking about the quality of being easy to see or hear or understand. And things that interfere with that ability to see, hear or understand clearly are clutter, chaos, and drama—in your mind or in your life. Interestingly, these things tend to go together. People with cluttered, chaotic lives rarely have tidy homes and well-organized daily schedules.

Where can you clear the clutter, chaos, or drama from your life? It's difficult to focus on what's important when clutter surrounds you. Of course, I am not speaking strictly of physical clutter, although a messy desk with piles of paper and dirty dishes from eating while you work does not make for an efficient and organized workday. Same with mental and emotional clutter. What steps can you take to reduce the clutter and gain clarity on your priorities in your Fields of Play?

Another valuable concept is closing "open loops." Again, this can mean a lot of things. It can mean all those things in your to-do list that are hanging out there and not getting done. Or all the windows you have open on your computer. Or the emails that you need to respond to, the phone calls you need to return, the bills you need to pay. You get the picture. Those open loops sap your energy. You know how good it feels to cross things off your to-do list. Closing open loops gives you the same sense of accomplishment, plus it frees up mental energy and reduces the clutter in your life. What about priorities? That sounds pretty straightforward, right? I'd be willing to bet you think you know what your priorities are. Take a moment to think about what are the top priorities in your life? What do you value? Try to be specific.

Now, how do you know what your priorities *really* are? You can find the truth in two places—your calendar and your financial statements. What you spend your time and your money on *are* your priorities despite what you may think.

In my journey to claw my way back from the brink of burnout, the fundamentals—nutrition, exercise, and sleep—were critical stepping stones, and adding a regular meditation practice was the secret sauce.

But understanding the concept of boundaries helped me turn the corner. I realized boundaries were drawn as the result of what/ created and what / allowed. I embraced the notion that I was "ridiculously in charge" of my own time and energy management and acted on that wisdom.

At work, I quit accepting meeting requests for after-hours meetings and quit answering emails on evenings and weekends. I started questioning if I even needed to be involved in all of those endless meetings. I analyzed my value at work and how to best spend my time. I got better at delegating work and decisions that did not require my expertise. I scheduled high-priority self-care time, including time for exercise and meditation.

I literally block time on my calendar during my workday to ensure that I get these activities in daily. Scheduling time for self-care increases my productivity exponentially compared to the time spent on the activity. I did this by focusing on what I have control of that directly impacts my desired results.

If you are struggling with overwork or overwhelm, please don't skip this step! There is much value and freedom to be found in managing your energy through the appropriate use of boundaries, clearing the clutter, and closing open loops. Don't think that just because you have to answer to someone—we all answer to someone—that you can't define your own boundaries. You absolutely get to choose what you are willing to allow, and you have more power than you think when it comes to what you can create in your life.

Next, we'll dive into mindset and behavior, the next two pieces of the puzzle, with some insights on how to hack your thoughts, emotions, and behaviors.

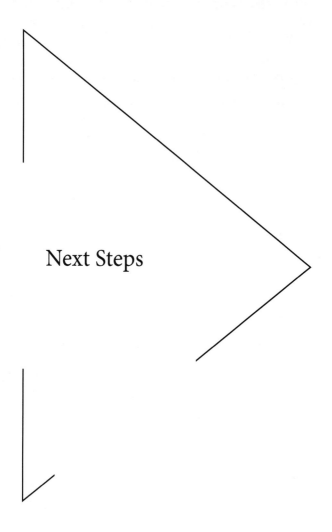

Next Steps

Write out a list of your top priorities in your life.

....

....

....

....

....

....

....

....

....

....

....

....

....

....

....

....

....

....

....

....

....

....

....

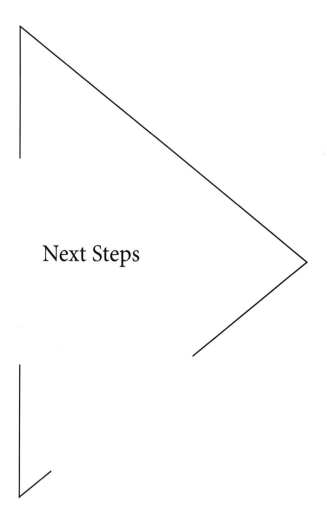

Next Steps

Now, take a look at your calendar and your financial statements—checking accounts, credit card statements, and so on. What do you spend the majority of your time and money on?

....
....
....
....
....
....
....
....
....
....
....
....
....
....
....
....
....
....
....

What you spend your time and money on are your priorities despite what you are telling yourself.

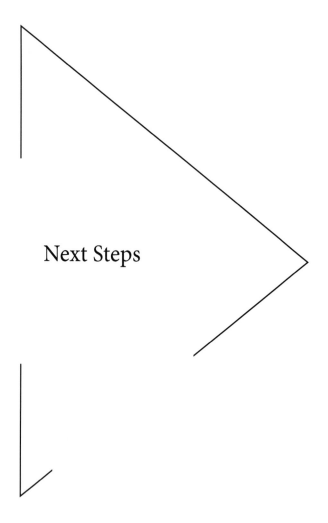

Next Steps

Did your calendar and financial statements align well with your identified priorities?

....

....

....

....

....

....

....

....

....

If so, bravo to you! If not, think about how you can be more intentional about shifting your time and money toward the things that are most important to you.

....

....

....

....

....

....

....

....

....

....

....

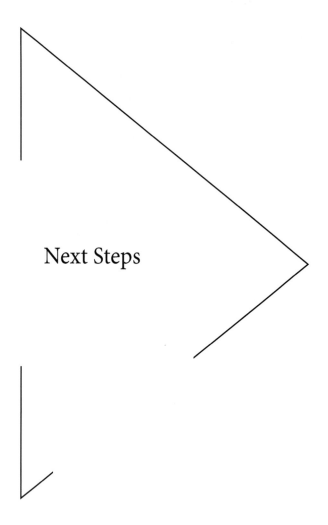

Next Steps

Now, use your calendar—digital or old school planner—to intentionally schedule all the activities that are important to you. These are your priorities!

Don't forget to include time for exercise, your meditation or stress management tool of choice, free time, doctor's appointments, grocery shopping, mealtimes, sleep, etcetera. If you don't schedule it, it won't happen!

Each Sunday evening, or first thing Monday morning, plan out your daily schedule for the week. And then stick to it. You'll be amazed at how much you get done when you have a schedule and have planned for everything you need and want to get done each week.

Part Four: Hack Your Way Back

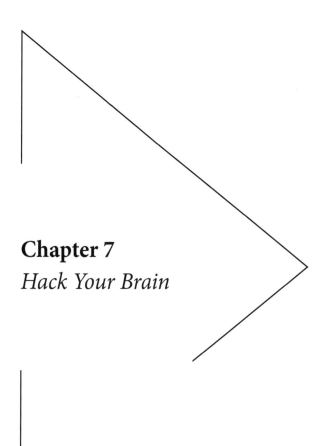

Chapter 7
Hack Your Brain

As defined by Merriam-Webster, biohacking is a term used to describe the use of science and technology to make your body function better and more efficiently. And while I haven't labeled it as such, the actions, tools, and techniques described so far in this book are all a form of biohacking—making your brain and body more resilient and higher functioning. In this chapter, we dive into hacking your brain. Thoughts. Emotions. Actions. Results. Your brain is the key.

Hack Your Thoughts

Whether you think you can or you think you can't, you're right. ~ Henry Ford

Let me let you in on a little secret. Your brain is a liar! That's right. It lies to you all the time. It tells you that you're not good enough, that you're not smart enough, that you'll never lose the weight, that other people are so much more _____ than you—fill in your own blank here. It tells you that everyone else has it all together and that you, dear self, are a basket case.

Why does it do this? Your brain craves the status quo. It will go to great lengths to "protect you" from change. It views change as the enemy and goes into auto-preservation mode. Sometimes our brain can be our own worst enemy. These self-sabotaging thoughts are often referred to as automatic negative thoughts or ANTS. And these negative thoughts, repeated over time, can turn into limiting beliefs.

We all have ANTS. The brain does this automatically. However, empowerment arises by recognizing ANTS for what they are and then replacing them with more productive thoughts based on reality that better serve us. ANTS are commonly described in relation to the cognitive-behavioral model or cognitive behavior therapy (CBT). CBT is based on the concept that our thoughts (cognition), feelings (emotion), and how we act (behavior) are all interrelated. Our thoughts create our feelings which drive our behavior.

The good news is you can retrain your brain to rewire

limiting thoughts and beliefs. One way to retrain your brain is to challenge the negative thoughts through a model called *The Work* by Byron Katie. This model has four questions, but I have found that the first two usually get you to the answer for simple ANTS. For deeper rooted or more ingrained limiting beliefs, you can use the full series of four questions.

When you have a negative thought, ask yourself, "Is this true?" If you answer yes to the first question, the next question is, "Can I absolutely know this is true?" In many cases, the answer to the second question is no. Our brain has a lot of opinions that aren't factual, and therefore are not true.

For example, if I have the automatic negative thought, "This is too hard. I can't do this." I would ask myself, is this true? Now suppose my immediate knee-jerk response is yes. Then I would ask myself, "Can I absolutely know this is true?" My answer here would have to be…no! When I begin to think about it objectively, I realize this may be hard, but I can do hard things! I've done things much harder than this in my life, and I can figure this out.

The Work by Byron Katie
1. Is it true?
2. Can you absolutely know that it's true?
3. How do you react? What happens when you believe that thought?
4. Who or what would you be without the thought?

The CBT approach to reframing the ANT would look something like this: identify the negative thought—"This is too hard. I can't do this." Then design a new thought that is accurate and productive—"This is hard, but I *can* do this. I've done much harder things in the past."

Why is it important to hack your thoughts? For one thing, your thoughts determine your results. More specifically, your thoughts create your actions, and your actions lead to your results.

But there's also an in-between step related to emotion. Your thoughts about something create an emotion or feeling inside you. Based on that emotion, you take action. Sometimes action means making a decision or taking physical action. Sometimes it means a *reaction* to the emotion, or it can mean choosing not to do anything at all, inaction. Your actions, driven by your thoughts and emotions, determine your results or outcomes. So indirectly, your thoughts determine your results. These concepts are commonly used in modern coaching techniques, but their origins are rooted in ancient wisdom.

If you struggle with negative thoughts, ruminate on decisions resulting in inaction, or generally feel stuck, consider working with a coach. Working with a coach can show you how your thoughts get in your way, and your coach then helps you learn how to change your thoughts, which will change your results!

Hack Your Emotions

Developing a resilient mindset can help you live a life of your design. ~ Dr. Joan Rosenberg

I want to share with you three simple ways to hack your emotions. Let me be clear on emotions. I'm referring to the common everyday emotions or feelings that we all have that can sometimes trip us up or get in our way. I am not in any way referring to clinical emotional disorders that require care from a medical or behavioral health care professional.

Before we jump into the emotion hacks, I want to reiterate a basic concept mentioned briefly in discussing thoughts related to the cognitive-behavioral model. Clearly stated, *your thoughts*, rather than other people or outside factors, create your emotions.

You may think that the driver who cut you off in traffic today *caused* you to feel angry. But that's not the case. A car that pulled in front of you is simply a circumstance, an event. Circumstances are events or facts that we give meaning to in the form of our thoughts. When your brain responds to this circumstance with the thought, "What an idiot! He could have caused an accident," we generate the emotion or feeling of anger. If your brain had instead come up with the thought, "He must be in a hurry. I hope everything is okay," you would not feel angry. Thus, it's your thoughts about events and not the actual events themselves that create your emotions.

The first way to hack your emotions is to *feel* them.

Feelings are sensations in the body activated through neurotransmitters and hormones released by the brain. Feelings or emotions are triggered by your thoughts. Again, it's important to understand that another person or an external event or circumstance cannot cause any feelings inside your body.

We can have two different reactions to emotions or feelings in our bodies. We can resist them or allow them. When we resist an emotion, it gains strength and becomes magnified. It sticks around. When we allow an emotion, allow ourselves to feel it fully, it passes and fades away.

Many of us try to avoid feeling our emotions; it's as if we are scared of feeling them. Especially our negative emotions. I invite you to feel your emotions, even if it is uncomfortable or difficult at first. Dr. Joan Rosenberg talks about this in her method, *The Rosenberg Reset*. When you notice a negative emotion bubbling up, you choose awareness over avoidance. Allow yourself to feel the emotion in your body fully. Where do you notice it—in your throat, chest, stomach?

The waves of difficult emotions generally last ninety seconds or less, and learning to ride the wave helps you master your emotions. You become less scared to feel them as you learn that they pass relatively quickly, and you can often learn something from them. You can learn more about this method by watching her TED Talk or from her book, *90 Seconds to a Life You Love*.

The second way to hack your emotions is to *evaluate the thoughts* that led to the emotion.

You can hack your emotions by changing your thoughts. Challenge the ANTs, and determine if they are true. Then as necessary, replace them with more accurate and productive thoughts. This hack helps you alter how your body responds to thoughts, which, in turn, changes the resulting feeling or emotion and your subsequent actions and results.

The third way to hack your emotions is to *employ the fundamentals.*

As we covered in Chapters 2 through 4, the nutrition, exercise, and sleep choices you make affect your mood, feelings, and emotions. Remember the quote from Dr. Ratey about exercise being the equivalent of taking a little bit of Ritalin and a little bit of Prozac? In addition, we also learned in Chapter 5 that meditation can improve your mood. When your mood is improved, you are more likely to experience positive emotions, be less reactive, and have a better outlook.

And here's a bonus hack for you. Emotions are contagious! Research has demonstrated that within the brain are neurons called mirror neurons. Mirror neurons allow us to observe and simulate others' actions and facial expressions, as well as the intentions and emotions behind them. How cool is that? Emotions are contagious, so surround yourself with people who have the positive emotions, actions, and results that you'd like to experience and emulate.

Hack Your Behaviors
In any moment of decision, the best thing you can do is the right thing. The next best thing you can do is the wrong thing. The worst thing you can do is nothing. ~Teddy Roosevelt

One of the most effective ways to hack your behavior is to tackle your decisions. Daily we're required to make hundreds if not thousands of decisions. Don't think so? How many emails do you get a day between your work and personal email accounts? Each email you receive can require numerous decisions. Simply unsubscribing from email lists you no longer want to be on can eliminate significant clutter from your inbox, and clutter in your inbox translates to clutter in other places in your life.

Decluttering your inbox can reduce decision fatigue. Recall our discussion about adaptation energy from Chapter 1; decision fatigue saps your adaptation energy. So decluttering = less decision fatigue = *more* adaptation energy. More adaptation energy means handling the demands and stressors of life with greater ease.

Decisions move you forward.

Take action. Decisions move you forward. Open loops slow you down and cause you to feel overwhelmed and stuck. One of the best things you can do to get unstuck is to start taking action. When faced with a decision, make a choice—just one small decision—and act on it. You will either get the result you want or the lesson you need. The worst thing you can do is nothing; take it from Teddy Roosevelt!

If you feel stuck and have a hard time taking action, a coach may be able to help you. A coach keeps you moving forward with consistent, focused action as opposed to busy work. Taking action based on the intentional results you want to create, as opposed to the safe actions your brain wants you to take, is how you achieve those results.

Another way to reduce decision fatigue is to capitalize on the power of routine. Habits and routines are *automatic* activities wired into your brain—they don't require ongoing decisions, so naturally, they decrease decision fatigue. When you don't have to expend energy to make routine everyday choices, you retain adaptation energy in your bank and keep your battery charged.

Behavior Design and How to Hack Your Habits
We are what we repeatedly do. Excellence, then, is not an act, but a habit. ~Will Durant

I received a few pieces of advice in my early career that stuck with me and have become more powerful over time as I have gained my experience. One of those came from a seasoned mentor who told me, "If you want to help people change their behavior, you have to make the right thing to do the easy thing to do." I don't think he knew anything about the principles of Behavior Design at that time. I think that advice came from the wisdom of a long life and career in medicine while watching what caused change efforts—individual or institutional—to fail or succeed.

In my career in health care, I have repeatedly seen that providing information does not change behavior. If it did, no one would smoke cigarettes. The information and evidence against tobacco smoking are indisputable, and it's right there on the pack of cigarettes!

Rather than information, *emotion* is what changes behavior. A famous quote, often attributed to Maya Angelou but history documents similar sentiments from ancient wisdom passed down through generations, states, "People may forget what you said, but they'll never forget how you made them feel." This quote eloquently reaches the core of the idea; emotion rather than information triggers behavior change.

Behavior Design is a term coined by BJ Fogg, Ph.D. and his research team at Stanford in 2010. In short, Behavior Design is a set of models for thinking about human behavior that help people—both individuals and in organizations—succeed at changing behavior. These models and methods are backed by research from Dr. Fogg's Behavior Design Lab at Stanford. The core principles of Behavior Design center around helping people do what they already want to do and helping them feel successful in the process. Simplicity and emotion are keys to changing behavior.

The Fogg Behavioral Model outlines the three variables involved in ANY behavior; motivation, ability, and a prompt (B=MAP). These three variables have to converge at the same moment in time for the behavior to occur. You can reliably change behavior by understanding and influencing the motivation, ability, and prompt equation.

Tiny Habits ® is a proven method for designing and creating lasting habits based on Dr. Fogg's years of research in Behavior Design. But how did Dr. Fogg develop this groundbreaking method? He hacked his own behavior, of course! Then he began to share his method and subsequently coached more than 60,0000 people in his Tiny Habits method. The best part about this completely novel, research-based method is it takes motivation completely out of the equation. You heard that right—no motivation required! Tiny Habits works, and it's easy to learn, implement and stick with.

How can I be so sure? I have experienced the benefits of Tiny Habits firsthand! And as a Tiny Habits certified coach, I have personally coached clients in this method and witnessed the transformation in their lives over and over again. It's an easy-to-learn simple method that quickly provides people with hope and evidence that they can change their behavior, even if they have repeatedly failed with other methods. The true power of Tiny Habits is the momentum it creates and the transformation that occurs in people's lives as a result. And the beauty of this method is that it can be applied across any area of your life and to any behavior you want to change. It can even be applied to overcoming bad habits. For more information about Behavior Design and The Tiny Habits method, visit the book resources web page.

Now that you understand the basics about how to hack your thoughts, emotions, and behaviors, let's talk about another essential piece of the puzzle. Community. You don't have to do it alone. The journey is easier and more fun with friends and trusted allies.

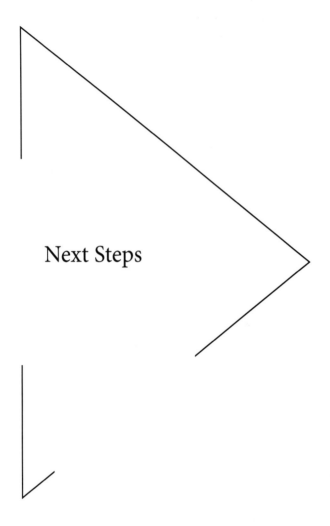

Next Steps

Hacking your brain can feel like some pretty heavy stuff, especially dealing with your thoughts and emotions. While this may feel less tangible than the other topics we've covered, it's equally important. Probably even more so. So, sit with these ideas for now.

Start to notice your ANTS.

....
....
....
....
....
....

What limiting beliefs tend to surface?

....
....
....
....
....

Start to notice when emotions come up for you throughout your day.

....
....
....
....
....

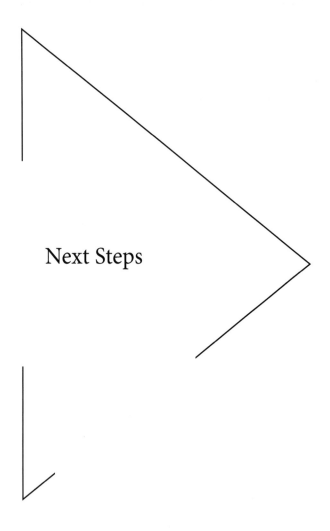

Next Steps

Pay attention to the thought that led to that emotion.
Notice where in your body you feel the emotion.
Name it. Is it anxiety, fear, sadness? Is it joy,
excitement, curiosity?

....

....

....

....

....

Start to notice when you avoid making decisions.
How often does this happen?

....

....

....

....

....

Start to notice when you avoid making decisions.

....

....

....

....

....

....

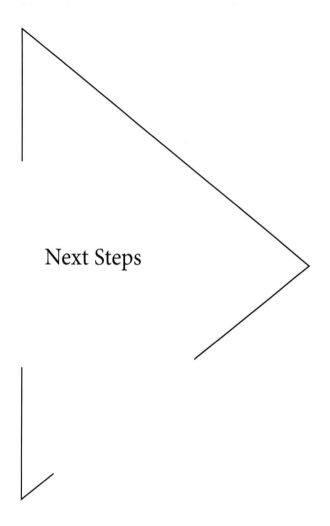

Next Steps

Start to think about the behavior changes you want to make but aren't acting on

....

....

....

....

....

....

....

....

What small (tiny!) steps can you take today to hack your habits?

....

....

....

....

....

....

....

....

....

....

....

....

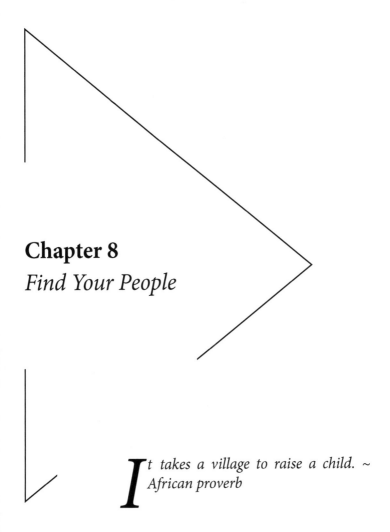

Chapter 8
Find Your People

*I*t takes a village to raise a child. ~
African proverb

As a working mom, you know the truth of this all too well. None of us can do it alone. Whether we rely on our spouse, family, friends, or paid support, we all need help along the way. While support is important, having a close circle of friends you can count on is about more than just support. Human beings are communal creatures. Your circle is a source of both social engagement and purpose, and these are two key indicators of happiness and well-being.

The way I see it, we all have the community we're born into—our family—and the loved ones we choose. Multiple opportunities arise for creating close relationships with others. Below lists five groups that you may consider your community or your support system.

First, let's talk about family. You have the family you were born into, your parents and siblings, and then you have the family you choose, your spouse or partner and children. While your family may support you in some ways, they are not always cheerleaders for *your* needs and *your* dreams—especially if the changes you want to make are not what they want for themselves.

Without getting too deep, I want to plant the seed that the reason to have multiple circles or communities is that you shouldn't expect all your needs to be fulfilled by a single person or group. If you are not finding the support you need in a particular area at home, look to your other communities and see where you can get that support from other allies and friends.

Beyond your family, the second most predominant place for connection and support is your social circle.

Your friends, co-workers, and acquaintances are your social circle. These are the people you spend time with, and you are influenced to some degree by their ideas and actions.

The next community to consider consists of your health care providers. This can include your doctors, therapists, and other health care professionals who help you stay healthy and provide care and support when you need it. As a smart, high-achieving perfectionist, you may think you can manage things independently or that you don't have time to get the care you need. You may even feel asking for help or managing your health proactively is a sign of weakness. Perhaps you think you can do some research on the internet and DIY this yourself. After all, who needs a real doctor when you have Doctor Google, right? Wrong! On one hand, you need to be an active partner in your healthcare and take accountability for your healthcare outcomes, but on the other hand, you need qualified, experienced, and trusted health care professionals to guide and support you in this process.

If you're exhausted, dealing with burnout, or have unexplained symptoms, get a comprehensive medical evaluation. Stress can cause many of these symptoms, but you need to make sure you do not have a medical cause or contributing factor that is treatable, such as anemia, a hormone imbalance, or nutritional deficiency. Start with your primary care physician. If necessary, consult with a Functional Medicine doctor as noted in Chapter 1.

A final community you may not have considered is

the group that supports or perpetuates your habits. This is a group of individuals who share the same lifestyle choices that you do. This could be a running club, a book club, a game night club, and so on. It could also be a less formal group—the women you take an exercise class with once or twice a week, the colleagues you go to happy hour with after work, or the people you run into in the park every day when you walk your dog or take your kids to play. As your children get older, this group may include the parents of the kids your children spend time with.

Your habit circle can also be a source of *identity*. When you join a running club and surround yourself with other runners, you acquire the identity of a runner. When your brain makes that shift to your new identity, it helps wire in the new habits more effectively, which is important if you want to wake up at 4:30 am to run before work. Your motivation to get up early to run will be zero on some days, but if your brain already sees yourself as a runner and you think this is just what runners do, it's not a motivation issue but a congruence issue. "I'm a runner, and this is what runners do, so I'm getting my rear out of bed whether I *want* to or not at this moment."

Here's one last word about habit communities. Remember you have a choice about who to spend your time with. Choosing friends and groups that support good habits, such as exercise or socializing, or bad habits, such as excessive drinking, gambling, or compulsive shopping, can make all the difference in the trajectory of your life. Choose wisely.

The last community I'll mention is your accountability

group. This can include both accountability partners and coaches. I'll start with the concept of an accountability partner. An accountability partner is someone you agree to connect with routinely; this person helps keep you on track toward your goals. This is often a friend or colleague and may be someone who has a similar goal they're working toward. It can be a one-way or two-way accountability partnership where you're both holding each other accountable. Knowing that you're accountable to someone can be an effective way to help you stay on track with your goals when you aren't getting there on self-discipline or willpower alone. Both accountability partners and coaches can be effective tools to help get you from where you are to where you want to be.

Coaches are professionals who help you get the specific result you want. They help you work through problems and decisions to achieve that result. They can also help you think differently about your circumstances, work through barriers, and serve as an objective and non-judgmental sounding board. You might hire a business or career coach to help you get promoted or advance your career or a health coach to help you overcome your struggle with weight and food issues. A habit coach can help you effectively form new habits in numerous areas, including exercise, weight loss, stress management, productivity, etcetera. A life coach can help with your struggles across numerous areas of your life, including relationships, work, health, and well-being.

Coaches help you clarify your goals, support you in taking decisive action towards your goals, and then hold you accountable for the choices you make. They are part teacher, part cheerleader, part tough-love coach, and fully invested in *you* and your personal growth toward your goals and desired results.

One major difference between a coach and a friend, family member, or even an accountability partner is that friends and family, even though they may have your best interests in mind, come with their own baggage. Their own opinions. *Their* own limiting beliefs. And they may give you advice that doesn't serve you based on their limiting beliefs and ideas. I'm not saying don't listen to your friends and loved ones. Of course, you should listen to them. But understand that their advice is merely an opinion, biased by their own world view. You get to decide.

As we close out the discussion on connection and community, I'm reminded of the famous Jim Rohn quote, "You are the average of the five people you spend the most time with."

This quote brings a couple of final lessons to mind. One, don't expect your spouse or any one person to provide all the support and encouragement you need. This is why building multiple support communities is invaluable. Two, not everyone will be on board with your plans. That's okay. Find your people that *are* on board and maximize your time with them. Minimize your time and, where possible, your commitments with those that want to squash your dreams or tell you that you can't create the life of your dreams.

Find your people.

Third, you, mostly, get to choose your people. Surround yourself with others who are living the healthy lifestyle you want to live. Spend more time with people who support your dreams and those that may already be living your dreams or at least taking inspired action toward theirs. Remember the concept of mirror neurons we discussed in Chapter 7. Success breeds success.

And finally, know that help is all around you. You just need to be willing to ask for it—and accept it. Remember, it takes a village...

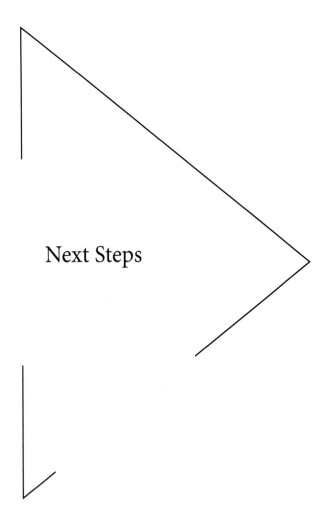

Next Steps

Evaluate your current communities and social circles.
List out the main members of each:

Family ....

....

....

....

....

....

....

....

....

....

Social ....

....

....

....

....

....

....

....

....

....

....

....

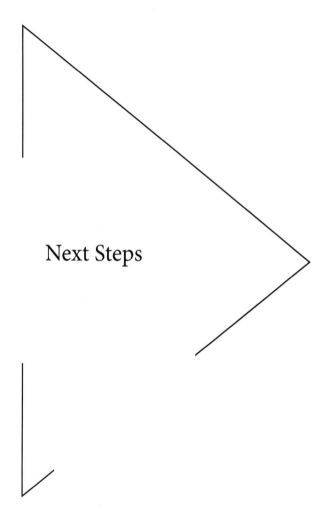

Next Steps

Health ....

....

....

....

....

....

....

Habit ....

....

....

....

....

....

....

Accountability ....

....

....

....

....

....

....

....

....

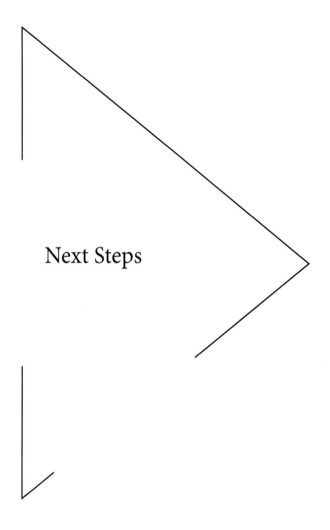

Next Steps

Which communities are robust and support you well?

....
....
....
....
....

Which groups have some gaps you need to work on?

....
....
....
....
....
....

Are there any support networks completely missing?

....
....
....
....
....
....

What small steps can you take today to ensure you have all the support you need to thrive?

....
....
....
....
....
....
....

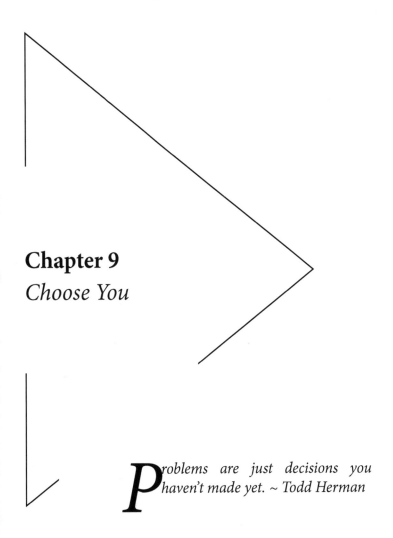

Chapter 9
Choose You

*P*roblems are just decisions you haven't made yet. ~ *Todd Herman*

As we reviewed in Chapter 6, one of the main causes of overwhelm is having too many open loops. Open loops are all those to-dos hanging out there waiting for you to take action to close the loop. Overwhelm can occur when you leave tasks hanging because you need to "think about" them before responding or taking action. What does it take to close open loops? It's simple. Closing open loops requires you to *make a decision*!

Each open loop requires one or more decisions to be made. As I write this, I have over twenty-five open windows on my computer. Now to be fair, over half of them are my book chapters, but clearly, this is an area I'm still working on! But I'm getting better, and it's about progress, not perfection, right?

Piles of mail? Open loops. Emails you haven't yet responded to or deleted? Open loops. Party invitation waiting for RSVP? Open loops. Deciding whether you'd rather take the 8 am or 10 am flight. Open loops. Ninety-nine times out of a hundred, delaying a decision doesn't make it any easier and can often make it harder. It definitely adds to the pile of open loops stressing you out, draining your adaptation energy.

Maybe you're currently doing well in some of these areas. You go through the mail as soon as it comes in every day. You pay your bills immediately. But perhaps your email inbox is another story. Or you have piles of magazines or catalogs with flagged pages for the items you *might* want to order. The solution to the open loops overwhelm problem? Make a decision!

As I learned from Todd Herman, "Problems are just decisions you haven't made yet." Make a decision and stick with it. Don't reconsider every little decision you make. With each decision, you either win, or you learn. You get the result you want or the lesson that you need. Most of the time, there *is* no right or wrong answer; that's what makes it hard to choose.

Do an open loop inventory and see where you could benefit from some tough love on your open loops. Decisions move you forward, and the only way to get unstuck is to move! Don't waste precious adaptation energy on open loops.

Put your own oxygen mask on first.

If you've ever flown on an airplane, you've heard this directive—in case of an emergency, put your own oxygen mask on first. Yes, of course, it applies to air travel, but it's also essential if you want to beat overwork, overwhelm, and burnout, to ultimately thrive. You can't take care of the other people and things that matter to you when you're drowning in your own river of misery. You can't bring your best self to work when you are your lowest priority. Agree to choose *you* first so you can show up at your best for the others in your life, in all your Fields of Play. And that starts with putting your own oxygen mask on first.

Four Decisions
Four major decisions will move you out of where you are now and on the road to where you want to be. These are all based on your willingness to prioritize *yourself.*

Decide to value your health.

Choose to fuel your body and brain with healthy, nutrient-dense food and skip the garbage that's easy, convenient, and addicting. Choose to make daily exercise a non-negotiable part of your day. Rather than two hours at the gym, shoot for thirty to forty-five minutes of exercise or activity most days. Taking a walk or playing outside with your kids counts. But even on extra crazy days, at a minimum, schedule a ten to fifteen-minute walk. Do it while making phone calls if you must multi-task. Choose to prioritize sleep. Make sleep your new superpower. Remember your brain takes out the trash during deep sleep, so pencil in seven to eight hours, eliminate the sleep thieves and create a simple sleep-enhancing bedtime routine.

Decide to value your sanity.

Choose to balance your adaptation energy through the day. Find at least one stress management tool or practice you love, and schedule it at least once daily—bonus points for twice a day! You don't need to meditate for two hours a day. Fifteen minutes of meditation twice a day restores your adaptation energy and boosts your productivity.

Get clear on your priorities and goals, and learn to say no to things that don't serve those highest priorities. You can do it all, but you can't do it all *well*. Boundaries, people! Boundaries will become your secret weapon.

Decide to change your mind.

Your thoughts determine your results. Decide to choose the thoughts that create the results you want. Decide to question thoughts that don't serve you.

Choose not to be afraid to feel your emotions. Your emotions are wise teachers. Feel your feelings and then question the thoughts that produced those feelings. First, you'll realize that you don't have to be afraid of your feelings, and second, by examining the feelings and what they might be trying to tell you, you'll gain valuable insight, which some would call intuition.

Decide to ask for help.

Choose to get by with a little help from your friends… and family, and your multitude of communities, as we discussed in the previous chapter. Choose to outsource things on your to-do list that don't require your skillset or expertise—things that you can hire out for less than your hourly wage such as running errands, grocery shopping, picking up dry cleaning, house cleaning, lawn care, the list goes on and on. Self-employed? Hire a virtual assistant to manage the routine and mundane tasks so you can focus your efforts on business-building activities such as creation and strategy.

Four Decisions
- Decide to value your health.
- Decide to value your sanity.
- Decide to change your mind.
- Decide to ask for help.

You can continue to do some of these things if you enjoy them and want to do them, but consider how your finite time is best spent. Spending fewer hours on less important activities means more time for self-care, more time with your loved ones, or more time pursuing your passion. Choose to spend time on things you value and outsource the rest.

Choose to hire a coach. Coaching can help you obtain your desired results much faster than you can manage on your own, and they can help you keep your thoughts in check so you don't get in your own way. All of these options create value beyond their financial costs. Choose to trade money for *value*.

Okay, this conversation's been fun, but it's time to wrap this up. If you're interested in learning more to support your journey, check out the resource page on my website www.BrainHealthMentor.com for a list of recommended reading. These are some of the best books and resources I've found in my own journey. Now, it's your turn to implement these ideas and transform your overwhelmed perfectionism into a healthy, vibrant, and balanced life!

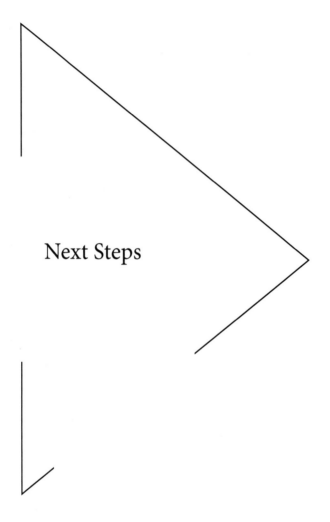

Next Steps

What open loops are cluttering up your mind right now?

....
....
....
....
....
....
....
....
....
....
....
....
....
....
....
....
....
....
....
....
....
....
....
....

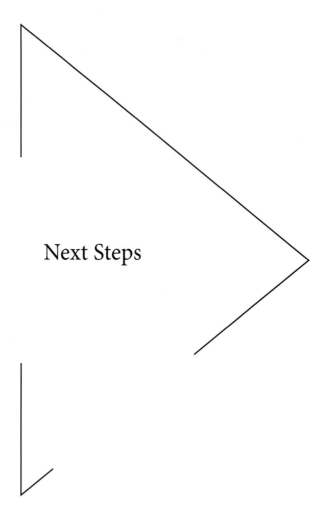

Next Steps

What decisions need to be made to move you forward?

....
....
....
....
....
....
....
....
....
....

What's stopping you from making these decisions?

....
....
....
....
....
....
....
....
....
....
....
....

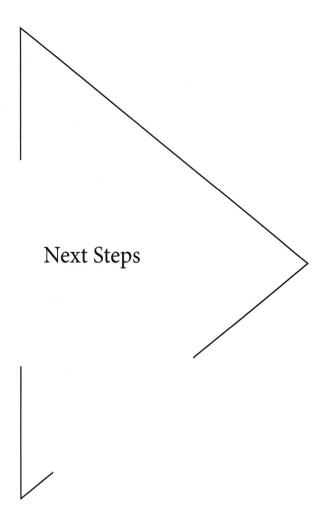

Next Steps

List three things you will start doing to value your health:

....

....

....

....

....

....

....

....

....

....

List three boundaries you will set to manage your adaptation energy and prioritize high-value activities:

....

....

....

....

....

....

....

....

....

....

....

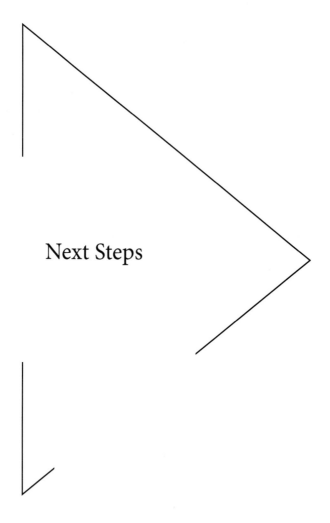

Next Steps

List three thoughts or limiting beliefs that aren't
serving you that you want to let go, and the thoughts you
will choose instead:

....
....
....
....
....
....
....
....
....
....
....
....
....
....

List three things you will delegate, outsource, or let
go of so you can focus on priority activities and tasks:

....
....
....
....
....
....

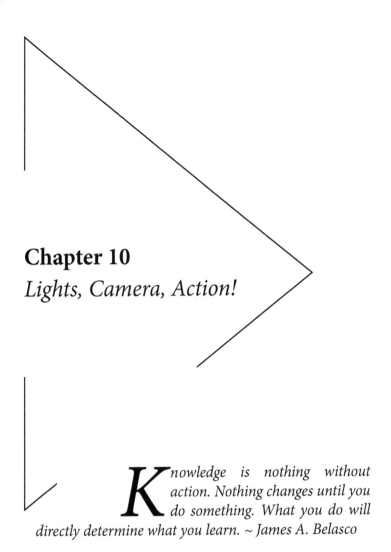

Chapter 10
Lights, Camera, Action!

*K*nowledge is nothing without action. Nothing changes until you do something. What you do will directly determine what you learn. ~ James A. Belasco

Get your rear in gear.

If you're a DIY type of gal, then you are all set. You now have the tools and the knowledge to get started on your road to recovery. It's time to take action. Start with the Next Steps questions and reflections in each chapter throughout the book. You can also find a link to a printable Companion Guide to this book with the Next Steps activities from each chapter on the book resources web page at brainhealthmentor.com/secrets-of-a-recovering-perfectionist/companion-guide/.

Taking action will get you from where you are now to where you want to be. Decisions and actions.

Start now.

Not next week, not next month. Not when the kids get out of school. Or when they go back to school. Now. How much time have you already spent in your river of despair? No excuses. You are the only one who can get *you* out of your current situation—stressed-out, burned-out, stuck, or overwhelmed—and into a life full of purpose, joy, and abundance. You either want to get better, or you don't want it badly enough to do something about it. Ready to get started but not sure exactly *how* to start? You can find additional resources on my website at www.BrainHealthMentor.com.

Start tiny.

Remember the principles of Behavior Design we reviewed back in Chapter 7. *Simplicity changes behavior.* So start with simple, tiny behavior changes that allow you to succeed, and create momentum for ongoing and bigger changes over time. Remember to celebrate your successes, no matter how small, because emotions change behavior, and this is how the brain wires in new habits quickly. If you'd like to learn more about the Tiny Habits method and try a free five-day digital coaching program with me, go to denee.choice@tinyhabitscoach.com

Start with the fundamentals.
Review the fundamentals we covered in Chapters 2 through 4. Making small changes in healthy eating, exercise, and sleep will bring about clear improvements in your energy and outlook. Then you'll be inspired to tackle other areas. Understand the importance of managing your stress and your adaptation energy throughout the day. Add a regular practice of meditation or other stress management practice that you love. This will help you perform at a high level, at work and home, without the frazzle.

Define your boundaries.
Remember, boundaries are what you create and what you allow, and they help you manage your energy. And energy, not time, is the fundamental element of high performance. Work on your mindset by hacking your thoughts and feelings. Understand how your brain works and learn to make it work *for* you rather than against you.

Get coached.
If you want a guide through this process, consider hiring

a coach who specializes in this area. Coaching is an evidence-based intervention for reducing symptoms of emotional exhaustion and overall burnout as well as improving quality of life and resilience. Even if you think you can do it yourself, a coach can help you get results *faster* and much more efficiently than you can on your own. Only you can do the work, but a coach will support you, guide you and keep you moving toward your goals. Coaching gets you moving and keeps you in massive action.

This is one area I wished I'd pursued sooner. I was making progress with my DIY approach. But my progress increased *exponentially* once I started working with a coach. I found clarity, understood how my brain kept me stuck by "protecting" me, and I found my path forward out of burnout and into a life of my choosing. My design. Once I saw the value of coaching—the deep, life-changing value—I decided to pursue coaching training and certification so I could help others who struggle with similar issues in their work and life.

Fun fact about the history of coaching, courtesy of Tony Robbins: "Know where the term Life Coaching comes from? If you think it comes from athletic coaching, it's actually the other way around. The term "coaching" developed at Oxford University in England in the 1830s, where it was used as slang for a kind of tutoring that would help students pass their exams. Why did they call it "coaching"? Well, if you had to travel in those times, to get from Point A to Point B, you would take a horse-drawn coach. So if you were going to London, you might "coach" to London. And if you were trying to pass your exams at Oxford University, you might "be coached" through your exams. For decades the term remained local slang. Then, when England began to professionalize sports, and they were looking for a way to describe a professional who helped athletes improve, they borrowed this term and invented the role of the athletic coach." Who knew?

Because of what I've learned and experienced on this journey, I'm all about brain health now. What is brain health? Brain health is emotional wellness. Brain health is developing stress resilience. Brain health is recovering from burnout and learning to thrive. But it's also so much more. Brain health is everything we talked about in this book. Every bit of it.

Your brain is the master organ, the captain of your ship. Everything you think, feel, do, and become originates in your brain. Brain health is about learning how to retrain your brain, so it works *for* you instead of staying in its default mode of trying to protect you by sticking to its default programming of seeking pleasure—sugar, alcohol, endless social media scrolling—avoiding pain—trying new things, having difficult conversations—and taking the easy route.

Once you understand how your brain works and its role in achieving or not achieving your goals, you can retrain your brain to produce the results you want in both your personal and professional life. And a coach can show you how. If what you've read in this book resonated with you and you'd like help implementing these strategies, I can help you with that.

This book lays out a framework. This framework changed my life and has changed the lives of my clients. And it can change yours. You just need to *decide* to change your life. You can do it! I know you can. Take the first step. I believe in the framework, and *I believe in you.*

Let me leave you with one last idea, the ripple effect. When you start making changes in one area, healthy eating, for example, and see the success and results it brings, you'll be inspired to make changes in other areas.

This happens, in part, because you have an identity shift. You start to see yourself as someone who can stick with new habits, someone who is a healthy eater, someone who exercises regularly, someone who creates boundaries. The list goes on. The ripple effect is not just an internal phenomenon; it works externally as well. As you focus on getting healthier, being more present in your relationships, and managing your energy effectively, people will notice. They'll want to know what you're doing. And they'll be inspired to start making changes in their life, too.

The smallest steps, taken thoughtfully and with consistency, will snowball into dramatic and meaningful changes in your life, far beyond the individual needle you are aiming to move today and far beyond your own personal transformation. I am excited for you to see your progress. Your success. And for you to witness how your changes influence the lives of others. That's the ripple effect.

If you'd like more support, encouragement, or help as you work through the framework, connect with me at denee@brainhealthmentor.com. I'd love to hear your stories about your journey and help you celebrate your successes. Now off you go. You got this!

Part Five:
Etcetera

Inspired to Learn More?

Recommended Reading

Tiny Habits Free 5-day Digital Coaching Program

Coaching, Consulting or Speaking

Recommended Reading
You can find my Recommended Reading list
on my website at: brainhealthmentor.com/secrets-of-a-
recovering-perfectionist/resources/

Tiny Habits Free 5-day Digital Coaching Program
If you're interested in learning more about Tiny Habits
and would like to try the free 5 day Tiny Habits digital
coaching program, reach out to me at denee.choice@
tinyhabitscoach.com

Coaching, Consulting or Speaking
To connect with me about coaching, consulting or speaking engagements, go to www.brainhealtmentor. com and fill out the Contact form, or email me at denee@brainhealthmentor.com.

Thank You For Reading My Book!

I hope you enjoyed it. Now that made it through, I would love your feedback. I need your input to make the next version of this book and my future books better.
Please consider leaving an honest review on Amazon.
Thanks so much!
Denee

Made in the USA
Las Vegas, NV
27 November 2023